BROKEN-HEARTED BELIEVERS

By the same author:

Moses: The Making of a Leader
Friends of God (with Jeff Lucas)
The Power to Persuade

Broken-Hearted Believers

CLELAND THOM

KINGSWAY PUBLICATIONS
EASTBOURNE

Co-published in South Africa with SCB Publishers
Cornelis Struik House, 80 McKenzie Street
Cape Town 8001, South Africa.
Reg no 04/02203/06

ISBN 0 85476 754 1

Designed and produced by Bookprint Creative Services
P.O. Box 827, BN21 3YJ, England, for
KINGSWAY PUBLICATIONS
Lottbridge Drove, Eastbourne, East Sussex BN23 6NT.
Printed in Great Britain.

*To my mum and dad, and brother, Alaster.
I am so grateful for their love and
influence on my life.*

Contents

Acknowledgements

I once heard a preacher saying that God existed as the Trinity because he did not want to spend eternity on his own. And I think there might be some truth in that. For God loves companionship – with his Son, Jesus, with his Holy Spirit and with his church. The Trinity is the greatest example of friendship that there is.

And when God created us, he did so in his image. In other words, he made us the kind of people who need friends. That's why he saw Adam with only animals for company and said, 'It is not good for man to be alone.'

I've found that without friends, you simply cannot make it through life, especially during the hard times . . . during those times when we have become Broken-Hearted Believers.

My wife Rachael and I have been through some desperate times over the last ten years or so. Times when our hearts were broken into what seemed like a million pieces. And it was God's grace, along with our friends, who got us through. Friends like Paul and Jan

9

Knight who never stopped loving us and believing in us, and produced champagne when there was absolutely nothing to celebrate. Friends like Alex Pett and Justin Blake, who prayed with us week in and week out when there wasn't a light at the end of the tunnel. Friends like Stan Warren, Frank Prideaux, Graham Kemp, Paul Ellis and their families, who helped to heal us and restore us. There are others, too . . . the list is a long one.

Frank Prideaux, Pastor of New Life Church, Emsworth, and John Martin, of Word of His Grace Ministries, gave considerable input into this book. Without their insights, wisdom and theological understanding, it would have ended up in the bin a long time ago.

To each and every one of them, I say 'thank you', even though the words are simply not enough.

I

The Emmaus Syndrome

'Jesus? Who cares about him?'

The two men trudged wearily along the bleak, rock-strewn road which wound its way from the bustling religious city of Jerusalem to the scenic village of Emmaus, around seven miles away.

Cleopas and his friend were heading home.

'A complete waste of almost three years, if you ask me!' grumbled the friend. 'I left everything I had to follow this . . . this Messiah. And now what have I got? Nothing! First we had John the Baptist. He baptised me in the River Jordan. He really gave us something to hold on to, the way he challenged that Roman puppet, Herod. God's first prophet since the days of Malachi, that's what everyone called him. I'll never forget the first time I heard him speak! He really laid it on the line about repentance, and I got baptised straight away. But what happened? He's dead – beheaded by Herod and that scheming wife of his.' He paused for a moment, trying to collect his jumbled thoughts. The road wound its way through rocks and parched green shrubland into the blurred, shimmering horizon.

'Then came Jesus,' he went on. 'The saviour of the Jews – the Messiah himself . . . the man to liberate us from the Romans, or so everybody said. But three years later, and now he's dead too. And me?' He paused again and thought for a moment. 'I might as well be dead too!' he said, rather lamely, unable to convey the turmoil which had been going on in his heart since Jesus had breathed his last on the cross in that dreadful execution just a few days earlier.

The men continued their walk in dejected, awkward silence for a while. Beads of sweat trickled down their faces as the sun beat down on them relentlessly from the deep blue sky. Their hearts were as heavy as their tread as they made their way down the long Roman road.

'What about the empty tomb?' asked the other man, Cleopas, tentatively puncturing the gloomy, despondent atmosphere. 'Everybody's talking about it at the moment.'

'Who knows? Who cares?' muttered his companion. 'Maybe the body was stolen. Maybe the Romans put it somewhere else to avoid more trouble from the different Jewish groups. Maybe it's all just a rumour – there's enough of them going round Jerusalem at the moment, that's for sure. Everyone's got their own story, from the Roman guards to the priests, Sadducees and members of the Sanhedrin. They're all full of it. All I know is that I gave up my home, my job, everything, to follow this so-called Messiah. I really thought he was going to redeem Israel, just as we've always been taught from the Scriptures. And now what have I got?' His voice trembled, wavering between tears and anger. 'Absolutely nothing.

Nothing to look forward to. No hope. And no future other than living a life at the beck and call of these Roman dictators. I don't know what to believe any more.'

He sighed and paused again for a while. 'What makes it worse,' he added, the tears really flowing now, 'was that I really loved him. And he loved me. I know he did. He proved it to me enough times. I just can't understand where it all went wrong.'

And the two men carried on walking . . . sadly and silently on the dry, dusty road to Emmaus, with nothing to look forward to but a dry, dusty future.

The Emmaus syndrome

The Bible is full of disillusioned people, just like those two men on the Emmaus road. You find them on almost every page. They may have walked closely with God and been great heroes of faith. They may have performed some awesome miracles, triumphed in battles and been success-ful in ministry. But at the same time they were often broken and despairing people – aspects of their characters that are all too often overlooked in our triumphalist, revival-hungry churches where perhaps many biblical figures would have been too weak and under-confident to qualify for a place on the leadership team.

Disillusionment has unquestionably been an uncom-fortable part of life for God's people since the beginning of time. No one could have messed up more spectacu-larly than Adam and Eve! They, more than any other people in human history, were the couple who had every-thing – and who needlessly and inexcusably lost it. They

couldn't blame their surroundings – they had a perfect
environment in the Garden of Eden. They couldn't blame
God – they had him as their personal friend and counsellor every evening. They could not blame their pasts or
their upbringings, for there were no hereditary sin problems to worry about. They couldn't blame each other,
although they eventually tried to, for they were both
perfect. They had the lot – even good jobs! Yet they
threw it all away in a few moments of naive and insane
disobedience. And who can envisage the fear that must
have engulfed them as they fumbled to sew some fig leaves
together to cover their nakedness and then ran and hid as
they heard God approaching? And who can imagine the
crushing despair that must have overwhelmed them as
they were cursed by God, given a life sentence of hard
labour and then banished from that beautiful garden for
ever? Disillusionment must have haunted them for the
rest of their lives, especially as they watched the dark
consequences of their actions insidiously working in their
own children and in God's beautiful creation.

The Egyptian slave Hagar knew all about disillusionment too. Her life was one which was wrecked by
circumstances and by other people. She seemed to live
permanently in the valleys. First she had to suffer the
indignity and upheaval of being sold as a slave and taken
from her homeland by Abraham and his wife Sarah, a
wealthy Hebrew shepherd family who had no business in
Egypt anyway. As the years went by she became innocently drawn into an emotive domestic issue, and paid a
heavy price for it. Abraham's wife Sarah had been unable
to conceive a child, but both she and Abraham were
holding on to God's promise that they would one day

have children of their own. However, as time went on
they had their doubts, like we all do, and so Sarah
decided to take things into her own hands – again, like
we all do! She opted to follow the local customs of the
time and persuaded Abraham to have a son through
Hagar. So Abraham slept with Hagar and got her pregnant; but afterwards the two women quite understandably
fell out, and Sarah went on to mistreat Hagar to such
an extent that she ran away. Who can blame her?
However, God intervened and commanded her to
return to Abraham's clan, which she did, and she later
bore Abraham's son, Ishmael.

Sarah eventually became pregnant in her old age and
Isaac was born to fulfil God's promise. But ill-feeling
between Sarah and Hagar continued to fester and eventually blew up, as these things often do, at a family get-
together. The young Ishmael was so badly behaved
during a big feast to celebrate Isaac's weaning that Sarah
ruthlessly organised Hagar's expulsion from the household – much against the wishes of Abraham who must
have known, deep down, that he was as good as signing
her death warrant. He might have been a man of faith, but
he was very weak when it came to dealing with his wife,
it seems.

Hagar, both a lone parent and a surrogate mother, took
young Ishmael into the bleak wilderness of Beersheba
with as much food and drink as they could carry between
them in stone bottles and tattered goat-skin bags. After a
few days of struggling to survive in the hostile wastes their
supplies were used up and they were becoming danger-
ously dehydrated – an ever-present threat in the desert.
So Hagar laid Ishmael under a bush in the shade and sat,

rejected and alone, a short distance away, weeping incon-
solably as she waited for her son to die a slow and
scorching death. Although God miraculously intervened,
as he often does when we are at our lowest and most
vulnerable, Hagar's struggles remain only too real and
only too awful.

Abraham's grandson Jacob too went through the same
loneliness and pain at the hands of his family. His mother
Rebecca persuaded him to deceive his father Isaac into
giving him the blessing which was rightfully due to his
older brother Esau. Impatience is not a new characteristic
among God's people! When Esau found out, he began
plotting to kill him, and so Jacob, like Hagar, ran away.
Like most people who run away from situations, he
ended up totally alone. And what a place to hit the
bottom! Luz, as it was called then, is one of the most
desolate places on earth: stark, gloomy hills dotted with
coarse clumps of thorns poking through piles of ragged
grey stones. No wonder Jacob had to use a rock as a
pillow – it is unlikely anything else was available. God's
promises for his life could not have meant much to him
then as he lay alone under the stars in this craggy,
unfriendly place, listening to the screeches of wild animals and fearing attack by bandits. And although, like
many other unpleasant places, it became the spot where
the heavens literally burst open above his head, he still
had to endure long years of toil and disappointment
before seeing even a hint of God's blessings come to
fruition. Like the rest of us, he had to face the consequences of his own actions – and found it difficult.

As for King David, what a warrior! He started his
career spectacularly, claiming the scalp of the seemingly

invincible Philistine Goliath, and later went on to enjoy such success on the battlefield that people sang of his fame. But even though he had been anointed king, he still reached unimaginable depths of despair, recorded in Psalm 142, after being pursued by the mad and raging King Saul, and again later after committing adultery with Bathsheba and cynically arranging the death of her husband.

And we must not forget Joseph, Ruth, Elijah, Jeremiah and countless others too: all Old Testament heroes who suffered long periods of pain and tears as part of their successful ministries and faithful walks with God.

You find disillusioned people in the New Testament too. Peter made a complete fool of himself by cutting off a Roman soldier's ear when Jesus was arrested in the Garden of Gethsemane. Then he went through the most horrible shame after denying to a harmless servant girl that he knew Jesus, just hours after confidently promising that he would follow him, even if it meant dying in the process. And Paul, one of history's most successful evangelists and church planters, went through the most testing and extreme pressure. 'We were under great pressure, far beyond our ability to endure, so that we despaired even of life,' he told the Corinthians (2 Cor 1:8).

Yes, discouragement, despair, disillusionment and disappointment often seem to be in there, right alongside blessings, successes and victories. You cannot have one without the other. And teaching otherwise produces broken-hearted believers. There are plenty of them about!

Disillusionment and discouragement have been the deadly enemies of God's people for centuries, and they

still are. They will stop any Christian from entering their
promised land and must be overcome time and time
again in our Christian lives. God went out of his way
to warn the newly appointed Jewish leader Joshua about
them before he finally led the Jews into the Promised
Land. Although he gave him a rousing pep talk before
he embarked on the exciting adventure across the River
Jordan and on towards Jericho, he also gave him a clear
warning: 'Do not be terrified; do not be *discouraged*'
(Josh 1:9, my italics).

The Hebrew word for discouragement is *chathath*,
meaning to be broken, confounded, or dismayed . . .
demoralised to the point of panic. So why did God sound
this sombre warning note, just as his people were about to
fulfil their destiny after forty years of aimlessly going
round and round in circles in the scorching desert?
Simply because he understood the pressures, problems
and failures that lay ahead and knew only too well that
the Jews would never survive unless they were prepared
to cope with both the bad times as well as the good.

Yes, Canaan was certainly a fertile land, overflowing
with milk and honey, and yes, God had already guaranteed his people victory over their enemies so they could
establish themselves as a new nation-state. But he
certainly didn't promise his people a feather-bed existence – far from it. So he went out of his way to prepare
them for the trials and difficulties in advance. He did not
allow them to have false expectations. Despite this
preparation, Joshua still had his wobbly moments, like
the time he blurted out to the Lord, 'Why did you ever
bring this people across the Jordan to deliver us into the
hands of the Amorites to destroy us? If only we had been

content to stay on the other side of the Jordan!' (Josh 7:7).
Joshua was also plunged into a pit of despair after an
unexpected defeat in battle by the Amorites – just at a
time when his fame was spreading right across Canaan.
He had to learn, as we all do, that set-backs and defeats
are a normal part of our walk with God, for God does not
measure success by our triumphs but by our faithfulness.
That's why, I believe, he said that he was 'well pleased'
with Jesus at his baptism – *before* he started his ministry.
He was pleased with the faithfulness he displayed by
working hard in his father's carpentry shop during those
early years. That's why the master in the parable of the
talents praised his servant for being 'good and *faithful*'
rather than successful or shrewd. Noah's ministry only
comprised looking after a handful of family members and
some animals. But he carried out his responsibilities
faithfully and God honoured him for it.

Those of us who, like Joshua, are advancing into our
promised lands just as fast as we can, need to be just as
attentive to the Maker's instructions. Yes, the land we
hope to possess is just the same for us as it was for the
Jews: it's full of blessings, challenges and opportunities; a
place where God can perform miracles, defeat our
enemies, transform lives and establish and advance his
kingdom on the earth.

But it is full of pressures, problems and traps too.
There are powerful and experienced enemies who will
not give up without a fight. There are walled cities – the
Jericho situations, or strongholds in our lives – which
seem insoluble and closed off to God and his church,
even with prayer and fasting. There are the secret sins
which eventually control us and destroy us, as they did

Achan, and which were responsible for that defeat by the Amorites. There are our natural human emotions which are notoriously fickle and prone to discouragement and fear. And there are Satan's forces – millions of demons who are committed to opposing, condemning and para- lysing God's people whenever they can, and who will need to be confronted strongly, persistently and author- itatively in the name of Jesus before they eventually flee.

We need to be properly prepared for these things, because the dangers have not changed in the last 4,000 years. The devil doesn't need any new tricks – the old ones work only too well. And we as God's people haven't changed much either. We might be filled with the Spirit and confident of God's power and authority in our lives, but we still tend to be stiff-necked – set in our ways and determined to do our own thing, like the Hebrews of old. Our humanity is still weak and vulnerable: the Psalms say we're made of dust, and that's exactly what we are. God remembers this, but we tend to forget. We slip into the belief that it is we who are infallible rather than God and his word, becoming very discouraged when we come a cropper and find it hard to get motivated again.

The Christian landscape these days is littered with people – good people – who weren't properly prepared to deal with disillusionment when it hit them. Many of them were not told it was not just a possibility in the Christian life, but a cast-iron certainty! You can spot them in many churches, if you look carefully. Sure, they're doing all the right things, maybe saying the right prayers, using the latest Christian buzz-words. Perhaps they're on the leadership team. Perhaps they're even the leader, pastor or vicar! But it doesn't take a great deal of discernment to see that in reality they're just going through the spiritual motions and that their zeal, their passion and their walk with God came to a shuddering standstill a long time ago.

It happened to a good friend of mine. Twenty years ago he was playing a significant part in his local church. He ran the youth group, discipled many young people and was a pillar in the congregation. He was instrumental in my becoming a Christian. But he became disillusioned with the abuse he took from some friends when God filled him with the Holy Spirit, and eventually left the church. He has only occasionally been inside one since. How sad. He was a real man of God whom I respected enormously. But that's the problem – he *was* a man of God. But not any longer.

Another man I know gave up on church life completely too. He left a promising career to obey God's call to lead a congregation and carried out his duties faithfully, and quite successfully, for a number of years. He paid a heavy sacrifice, as most leaders do, with his wife and children bearing the brunt of his ministry. And then one day a remote apostolic figure decreed that he should step aside and hand the church over to another, more gifted brother. He did so – and ended up without a job. He signed on the dole and eventually lost his house because of financial hardship. Disillusionment dealt him a blow from which he has still not recovered.

Revival sickness

We are currently living in times when the church is optimistically looking ahead to a revival, when God pours out his Spirit on the nation in the way he has done many times in the past. Many churches are preparing for revival as if it were just about to start. And maybe it is! But what if it isn't? It is easy to shout down people who ask questions like this. But we need to ask ourselves how people will handle it when the excitement of the latest wave of blessing dies down and they are left scratching their heads and wondering if those rumours of revival were just that – rumours and nothing else, with good times around a corner which never seems to get any nearer?

My concern is that Christians across the country have been waiting and praying for revival for so long that they are in danger of giving up. They have had almost ten years now of praying for revival, being trained for revival, reading about revival, and of course hearing tales of revivals which always seem to be happening somewhere else . . . in fact anywhere else other than where they are living! And the result is that many of them are becoming weary and discouraged. Their hopes are repeatedly raised and then dashed and as a result their hearts are becoming sick, just as King Solomon warns in Proverbs 13:12 where he says, 'Hope deferred makes the heart sick.' For while all the prayer, talk and preparation can be inspiring in some ways, it can also become thoroughly depressing if the revival never seems to happen. It is a bit like training and preparing for the FA Cup Final year in and year out, but never actually playing the game!

Now, waiting and praying for revival are not necessarily problems in themselves. Most revivals are preceded by years, decades even, of painstaking and persevering intercession. And this is good, for God will always give his people grace to persevere. However the greater danger comes when people, especially leaders and pastors, are too free with their promises of when those prayers will be answered. Disillusionment is the unavoidable result. A pastor or leader who makes rash promises but then cannot deliver the answer will soon discover he has a disillusioned and unsettled congregation.

Throughout this decade a number of significant prophecies have been given which actually specify the date when revival will start in this country, and the disillusionment which eats away at many people when it clearly doesn't happen still leaves its mark to this day. Of course, some try to explain the situation by saying that revival *has* started, and that people who do not agree are simply lacking in faith. But that simply doesn't wash with the many people who have seen revivals before, or read accounts about them, and who have realised that, although many good things have been happening across the country in recent years, we have certainly not seen anything remotely resembling the outpourings of the Spirit and the outbursts of God's glory seen by John Wesley or the Jeffreys brothers in previous generations. As a result many people have become deeply suspicious of the prophetic ministry when it is used as a diary in this way and are weary and cynical about the whole concept of revival.

In an attempt to counter this problem, some churches try to 'hype' things to create the appearance of revival in order to prove that something is indeed happening. But this man-made hype doesn't last long, bears little fruit, unsettles people and can draw people off into all kinds of strange and deceptive spiritualities which are put down, undiscerningly, as manifestations of the Holy Spirit's power.

It is also a fact that many churches believe they have received prophetic words that revival is going to start with themselves. I visited three within a month once, and they had all had the same word! They cannot all be right – and how are the ones who are wrong going to cope with the inevitable sense of let-down? History tends to show that revival starts in the churches which don't expect it rather than in the ones which do! The ones that don't expect it are the ones who are empty enough to need refilling, and who cry out to God to revive them because they recognise their nakedness and inadequacy. Perish the thought that we could become like the church in Laodicea, which did not realise that it was 'wretched, pitiful, poor, blind and naked' (Rev 3:17). Churches that recognise their own sorry state are usually humble enough to cope with revival when it comes and takes them completely by surprise. Nobody is entitled to revival, and it concerns me that many modern churches treat it as though they are. It is not something that can be earned, and while prayer always precedes revival, that does not mean that just because we have prayed, God will send it. If that were the case, revivals would be an act of our sovereignty, and not God's. I do not believe this is the case.

Webster's dictionary defines 'revival' as 'Return, recall or recovery to life from death or apparent death . . . from a state of languor . . . from a state of neglect, oblivion, obscurity or depression. Renewed and more active attention to religion: an awakening of men to their spiritual concerns.' Revivals change dormant churches into militant ones. And churches that are boldly and confidently claiming and expecting revival are not dead, or in a state of neglect, oblivion or depression. Far from it! They are alive and strong, but perhaps too much so for their own good. History tends to show that revivals are an act of God's mercy and grace, and can certainly never be written in anyone's diary or inserted in the church's five-year plan. To treat them in this way borders on the proud – a characteristic which God always resists. The timing needs to be left to God. You don't often find prophecies in the Bible which give times and dates and we should be cautious when such words are given to our churches.

My feeling is that a revival in Britain is a way off, and this nation will have to endure many times of deep grief like ones we have experienced over the last three years before people's hearts are soft and desperate enough to receive the gospel.

Britain will, I believe, only see revival after the church has been broken of its adolescent strength by a period of testing, tears and persecution. At the moment, we are in our teens: strong, enthusiastic, full of youthful arrogance and ready to take on the world and the Devil, and maybe even the flesh! But perhaps we are forgetting that God only uses broken vessels and that he will only send revival when two things happen: first, when the moral, spiritual and political climate of the country has reached a state of complete darkness and depression; and secondly, when Christians are so moved by their own sinful, worldly and remiss state and by what they see around them that they are driven to pray as if their lives depended on it. Does your church prayer meeting reflect this fervour? Probably not!

The great revivalist Charles Finney once said, 'Sometimes the conduct of the wicked drives Christians to prayer, breaks them down and makes them sorrowful and tender-hearted, so that they can weep night and day and instead of scolding the wicked, they pray earnestly for them. Then you may expect a revival.' I personally do not believe that either our nation, or our churches, are anywhere near ready for revival, and the more people say otherwise, the greater the disappointment will be.

I also believe that many of our churches are still too introspective to cope with a revival at the moment. There have been several significant outpourings of God's Spirit since the 1960s, and the one thing they have had in common is that churches, by and large, have absorbed them, like a sponge. By doing so, we have forgotten one of the basic principles of God's economy – that we should be freely giving away what God has freely given us (Mt 10:8). In soaking up God's power, in not taking it out onto the streets and into the community, we have become like the Dead Sea which stagnates because it has no outlet. The New Testament church had the same problem to an extent. They absorbed the outpouring of the Spirit at Pentecost and then by and large ignored Jesus' great commission to take the good news beyond Jerusalem for around fifteen years. It took a good dose of persecution by the zealous Saul to shake them out of their cosiness and scatter them into Judea and Samaria – the very regions which Jesus commanded them to go to before his ascension. Maybe our churches need a similar shake-up before we are prepared to take the fruits of the charismatic renewal and other outpourings of God's power out of our buildings and onto the streets.

A friend recently described his church's latest plan for midweek meetings. He was struggling to explain the difference between home groups, action groups, function groups, community groups and cell groups. After listening to him I laughed, 'Call them what you like. At the end of the day they will result in people sitting in someone's lounge drinking coffee.' Churches in Britain have been drinking coffee for around thirty years now while the moral state of the nation has steadily and alarmingly declined and the influence and status of other beliefs and religions have mushroomed.

Many people have assumed that the waves of blessing which many churches experienced during the 1990s were the early tremors of revival. But I believe we will look back in years to come and realise that they were, in fact, God's way of preparing us for some painful and difficult times ahead . . . times that will hurt and weaken us, and yet help us towards the maturity we will need when the Spirit's power finally rushes across the country. I could be wrong and, in some senses, I hope I am! But whether I am right or wrong, we need to strike a sensible balance between having faith for great things on the one hand and being realistic in our expectations on the other. We must learn how to avoid discouragement, to keep persevering and get on with the things of everyday life until revival starts . . . and indeed, how to continue doing these things when it starts. For even when our churches are pulsating with Pentecost power, we will still have to get up in the mornings, go to work and battle round the supermarket for our shopping!

Another aspect of revivals which we should be keenly aware of is that they always stop! Whether because of

God, or men and women, is a hotly debated point. But stop they do, whether they are personal, national or even global. The outpouring of God's Spirit in the book of Acts eventually faded away even though it lasted for a significant number of years. And even the final outburst of God's power which will precede the return of Jesus will stop when he does return! The problem is that if we look upon revival as the answer to all our problems, we are going to hit some desperate times when it disappears. We will only be able to cope if we have learned to walk steadily with God in the good times and the bad, during times of famine and times of plenty. If we rely on a revival to sweep us painlessly through our Christian lives, to solve all our problems and answer all our questions, we will eventually get a nasty shock when the power subsides and we are left with the nitty-gritty of everyday life to contend with.

Revivals need to be talked about, and prayed for, with extreme caution, not with rash and presumptuous boldness. They can be dangerous. Ask Ananias and Sapphira! James Burns, writing in *Revival, Their Laws and Leaders*, said in 1901,

> To the church, a revival means humiliation, a bitter knowledge of unworthiness and an open and humiliating confession of sin on the part of her ministers and people. It is not the easy and glorious thing many think it to be, who imagine it fills pews and reinstates the church in power and authority. It comes to scorch before it heals; it comes to condemn ministers and people for their unfaithful witness, for their selfish living, for their neglect of the cross, and to call them to daily renunciation, to an evangelical poverty and to a deep and daily consecration. That is why revival has ever

been unpopular with large numbers within the church. It says nothing to them of power such as they have learned to love, or of ease, or of success. It accuses them of sin, it tells them they are dead ...

Do you really want revival? Do I? I'm not sure. But I know one thing for certain — I am not ready for it yet.

Youth with a vision

It was another one of those revival prayer meetings, like so many others I had been to. I must admit I was weary of it and was finding it hard to stay awake. But something broke through my lethargy and touched my heart. Several of the church's young people prayed and called on God with tears and with a fervour and a passion that I had not heard for years. I recalled how I used to be just like them. That was fifteen years ago, before I had been through a church split, wounded by people's words, prayed for the sick many times and seen nothing happen, and had preached the gospel in endless meetings and yet seen few people saved.

At the end of that meeting the young people prayed for the older ones who, like me, had become stale and discouraged over the years. It was one of the most powerful and significant times of ministry I have ever experienced. It made me realise that there must be hundreds of people like me who caught fire during the charismatic renewal of the 1960s but who have now settled for middle-aged mediocrity or old-age obduracy. Maybe you're one of them. If you are, perhaps this book will help you.

2

Let's Get Real

The car was starting to make some strange grating sounds and black smoke was belching out of the engine. I'm no mechanic, but even I knew that something was wrong somewhere. I hesitantly asked my friend, who was driving, if everything was all right.

'Hmm,' he said. 'I should have known. The oil warning light came on the other day, but because I couldn't be bothered to change the oil, I took the bulb out. That way I stopped worrying about it.'

A great idea – until, of course, the car finally shuddered to a halt with a seized-up engine!

My friend might have been mad. But I couldn't really criticise him. After all, we all have our own ways of avoiding facing up to the unpleasant realities of life. I personally put off going to the cash dispenser to check my bank balance for days on end, simply because I cannot bear to see the news that I'm overdrawn yet again!

Many churches have, I believe, been avoiding facing the fact that for a long time now things have not been going too well. We have hoped for so much but in reality we have not seen a great deal. We believed we would see miracles, signs and wonders, and yet healings are still few and far between; many of us struggle to find a divine cure for the common cold, let alone anything worse! We believed that thousands of people would become Christians when we preached the gospel and yet at best there are occasional lasting conversions. We believed we would have a major impact on society and upon the nation; yet find that other religions carry more clout, where it matters, than we do and we are still standing by, apparently powerless, as the moral state of our nation steadily declines. We believed for massive growth and yet the statistics tell us that the numbers of Christians in this country have not changed over the last ten years.[1] And rather than face up to our sorry state, we have taken our bulbs out and avoided the cash dispensers. The result is that because many of us are frantically busy with a Christianity that in some ways appears good, but which is nowhere near as effective as we had hoped it would be, many are becoming tired and disillusioned.

Every time I have preached on disillusionment and disappointment over the past five years, the response has been enormous. Sometimes entire congregations have stood up to ask God to heal them. And this has worried me, for it surely cannot be a good thing that such large numbers of people are so discouraged. And it worries me even more that rather than learn from our mistakes, we are continuing to sow the seeds of disillusionment in years to come, not really perceiving our sorry state.

Disillusionment – the hidden snare

Disillusionment can strike swiftly. One moment, every-thing's fine, our hopes are high and God's blessings aren't just a theory, they are an everyday reality. Then we get an unexpected let-down or things don't go the way we expected, and everything turns sour. Our dreams die, our worlds cave in and our hearts break and quickly grow hard and cold.

Either that or it creeps up on us slowly. Criticisms, disappointments, rejections ... they secretly and insi-diously eat away at our hearts and our motivation while we gallantly carry on with our busy church lives, burying what we really feel. Until, one day, the straw finally breaks the camel's back and we say, 'Enough is enough.' I believe there are large numbers of disillusioned people around at the moment.

The problem is that they're trapped by their faith. They still believe that God is God, they love him some-where in their hearts, and they know that church is the right place to be. They are confident, deep down, that the Christian life is the right one for them and would not want to change it for anything else. But the reality is that they've found that the goods didn't match up to the advertising: that those Bible promises didn't seem to come true, those prophecies weren't fulfilled, those prayers weren't answered and those committed friends who spoke freely and lovingly about covenant relation-ships eventually let them down. And quite simply, they have never recovered from the experience. They cannot live without their faith – but cannot live with it, either. It's an awful place to be.

And then of course there are those who aren't in church at all any more. Ask around and people will tell you that perhaps they weren't saved in the first place . . . that they didn't really share the church's vision . . . perhaps they were goats and not sheep, or were fruit picked before it was ripe. But in reality, perhaps, they were so deeply disillusioned they simply gave up and there was nobody properly equipped or bold enough to get behind their 'No Entry' defence mechanisms to bring healing and restoration to their aching hearts and lethargic, paralysed wills.

Disillusionment can kill our spiritual lives and destroy our marriages, our jobs, our relationships, our churches, even our streams and our denominations too. And most, if not all Christians, suffer from it to some degree. In fact it's impossible to live a disillusionment-free life, and anybody who preaches differently probably hasn't lived a life of any real depth or significance. Itinerant ministers, especially those who are not properly rooted in local churches are prone to this: they lead such unreal existences on the road, going from one exciting meeting to the next, that they never face the difficult issues that the rest of us face. But we shouldn't be taken in by their shallow promises of instantaneous, glorious and victorious Christianity. There's no such thing – Jesus never led a life like this, the Bible does not promise one and we should not expect one. Such ministers would find the same themselves if they came off the road for a couple of years, did their own shopping every week on a frantic Saturday afternoon and did what the rest of us have to do – get on with their lives in the unpredictable and uncomfortable furnace of the local church.

A bed of roses?

One problem is that in our faith-filled, triumphalist churches, the concepts of suffering, of a God who breaks people in order to use them and who sometimes appears to let us down, are things that are left out amid the hype of a victorious Christian existence. Sometimes in the scramble to advance God's kingdom we preach a gospel that replaces the cross with not just a bed of roses but a box of them too – lots of nice treats with attractive wrapping round them! And then when people have to face some of the bitter realities of life, they are not ready to cope, blame it all on God and give up. Maybe they should have been taught more thoroughly at conversion that Christianity starts at the cross – the place of death; the death of our own plans, hopes, dreams and lives. And until we are regularly visiting the cross, there is absolutely no progress we will ever make in our Christian lives. So many people look at the cross, admire it, look beyond it, weep over it . . . anything, in fact, rather than embrace it and its implications for their lives.

Young people are particularly prone to disillusionment. In our eagerness to see them become Christians, we often over-state the blessings and don't say enough about the cost, the pressures and the sacrifices involved. I once heard an evangelist tell a teenager, 'If you give your life to Jesus, all your problems will disappear!' If only this were true. Very often, becoming a Christian means our problems are only just beginning, since when God really gets to work on our lives, it can be extremely painful and uncomfortable, although we do have the awesome advantage of having him alongside us helping to solve them. But answers like this cause disappointment; then we wonder why youngsters give up when the going inevitably gets tough sooner or later.

I once met a lady who genuinely believed that Christians should never suffer any problem for more than three days, since this was how long Jesus suffered during and after his death, before his resurrection! I wish she was right and that life could be the same as the Australian soap *Neighbours*, where people fall out irrevocably during Monday's episode and then make up again with moving soliloquies of apology on the Wednesday! The lady in question just couldn't comprehend that life just isn't like that – after all, the apostle Paul seemed to suffer almost without interruption from the day of his conversion to the day of his death.

> I have worked much harder, been in prison more frequently, been flogged more severely and been exposed to death again and again. Five times I received from the Jews forty lashes minus one. Three times I was beaten with rods, once I was stoned, three times I was shipwrecked, I spent a night and a day in the open sea, I have been constantly on the move. I have been in danger from rivers, in danger from bandits, in danger from my own countrymen, in danger from the Gentiles; in danger in the city, in danger in the country, in danger at sea; and in danger from false brothers. I have laboured and toiled and have often gone without sleep; I have known hunger and thirst and have often gone without food. I have been cold and naked. (2 Cor 11:23–27)

Hardly glorious, victorious, triumphant Christianity!

The sting in the tail

It's good, essential even, to go to a dynamic church where there are bold strategies, big ideas and great hopes of bringing the kingdom of God into our communities and into our towns; of tearing down the strongholds of sin and darkness and bringing in the rule of God. That's got to be a thousand times better than the no-hope-as-we-slide-down-the-slope existence that you find in some churches which never had the guts to get into the boat in the first place, let alone get out of it and walk on water! God wants powerful churches containing people of vision who are bold enough to plan for a great future and daft enough to possess it through prayer, faith and spiritual warfare.

But we also need to recognise that there is a sting in the tail if you are in a faith-filled church. The problem is that we are *believers*! And because we believe for so much, the chances of our being let down and disappointed are that much greater. Being a believer carries benefits and blessings – but huge risks too. In some ways, it would be easier and far more comfortable if we lowered our expectations and believed for less. People who do not believe in divine healing have no problems whatsoever when God does not heal them. They never expected him to do so in the first place. Nice and easy. But our problem is that we have had a revelation of God's love, healing power and desire to answer prayer, and once you have seen something, you cannot 'unsee' it. So we have to continue believing and hoping ... and being disappointed at times. For it's completely unrealistic to see every prayer answered, expect to win every battle, to see every project succeed and to come out on top of every situation. That's why Jesus stressed the importance of realistically assessing the odds before we go into battle or take on big projects. 'Suppose one of you wants to build a tower,' he told crowds of people following him. 'Will he not first sit down and estimate the cost to see if he has enough money to complete it? . . . Or suppose a king is about to go to war against another king. Will he not first sit down and consider whether he is able with ten thousand men to oppose the one coming against him with twenty thousand?' (Lk 14:28, 31).

Jesus constantly reminded his disciples that following him was not an easy ride (Mk 8:34). It's not lacking in faith or being pessimistic to look at some goals and situations and say, 'This one's beyond us.' And Jesus is no less Lord, and no less victorious, just because we stepped out boldly in his name and fell flat on our faces, or decided that a task was too difficult for us or beyond our level of faith, as the disciples did when they tried to cast a demon out of a young boy (Mt 17:16–19).

We need to understand that 'down' times are a completely normal part of everyday Christian life and to learn how to embrace them when they occur. Unless we do, we will end up like the two men on the Emmaus road: completely disillusioned and with shattered dreams, walking away from our friends, our calling, our vision, into an empty yet comparatively pain-free future.

God isn't fair!

Another problem with our triumphalistic Christianity is that we can easily forget that following God is guaranteed to involve suffering, and just because we are going through a painful or even unjust time does not mean that there is something wrong with us or our walk with God. When King Herod began persecuting the Jerusalem church in Acts 12, he arrested James, the brother of John and had Peter thrown into prison. Peter was miraculously released by an angel, while James was executed. Does that mean that Peter had more faith than James, or that James had some kind of problem which stopped him from receiving God's best? I don't think so!

It sometimes puzzles me why some Christians seem to have a very easy time of it, while others seem to lurch from one hardship to another. It does not seem fair and it is not meant to be. You simply cannot compare them. While God's promises are true and unchanging, his dealings with each of us are completely different, and we should not expect him to treat other people the same as he treats us. He won't. Although we are all equal in his sight, that is a matter of status and doesn't mean that we will get identical treatment to other people. I have three sons, and they are all equal in my sight. But they certainly don't get the same treatment! One of them goes to bed later than the other two – he is mature enough to cope with it. The oldest chooses, to a degree, what he wants to wear and how he conducts his social life. The youngest has most of these decisions taken for him. One obeys instantly and rarely needs disciplining. Another finds it difficult and gets punished more often. Yes, they are equal, but they need and receive radically different treatment.

The main cause of disillusionment

I've counselled countless disillusioned people over the years and in many cases you find that false hopes are the root of their problems. They expected one thing – usually quite unrealistically and without any genuine foundation whatsoever – got another, and were unable to cope with the consequences.

False hopes bring disillusionment in marriages. Women get married in the hope that their husbands will be kind, romantic, thoughtful, good listeners and generous enough to buy them plenty of new clothes. But when, six months after the wedding, they find that all Mr Perfect wants to do is sleep and watch football on television every Sunday afternoon, they end up disillusioned – perhaps with some justification! Perhaps someone should have warned them in advance that a fantasy super-hero husband was a rather unrealistic expectation and was a sure-fire way of becoming disappointed. Divorces often result from people having completely wrong expectations of their partners and then giving up and walking out when the bubble bursts. The reality is simply too awful to bear.

It happens in ministries. People hope and believe that God will use them to heal the sick, work abroad, go full time and preach at Spring Harvest – and when all they're doing six years later is putting out the chairs for the Sunday meeting they get so disillusioned they give up. Perhaps someone should have warned them in advance that their expectations were completely unrealistic and that they had neither the gift nor the character to fulfil their dreams.

Church splits often result from people having wrong expectations of how God is going to use them – particularly when they think they should be leaders and nobody else does! They become negative, critical, gather others around them (for disillusioned people always colonise) and, before you know it, you've got a division. And when you sit down and analyse their expectations with them, you normally find that they were based on virtually nothing at all other than a few vague and unreliable 'God told me' promises. Perhaps someone should have met them and discussed what they could *realistically* expect to do, along with a sensible timescale. That would have avoided a lot of hurt and problems later on. Without such safeguards, people often become so disappointed they walk out – and take a third of the congregation with them. You tend to find that most church splits involve around a third of the congregation leaving. That's been the pattern since before creation, when Satan, too, had aspirations above his station – and was thrown out of heaven with one third of the angels.

Disillusionment also occurs in our relationships with our leaders, vicars or pastors. We join the church and hope they will have the evangelistic anointing of Billy Graham, the caring heart of Mother Teresa and the leadership qualities of Moses. We expect them to visit us when we are sick, give to us when we are poor, pray for us when we are low and have the word of the Lord for us on tap whenever we need it. And when they don't fulfil these expectations, we become disillusioned and either leave the church or treat the leader badly, or both. But in fact we had no right to expect those things from them in the first place and certainly no right to demand that they live up to our expectations of them. Jesus is the only Good Shepherd. The rest are just trying their best!

You almost always find that whenever disillusionment rears its head, false hopes – or illusions, in other words – are the cause. Now, if you asked someone if it was sensible to build their life around illusions, they would certainly say 'No'. Common sense tells us this is unwise. But that's what we do in almost every area of our lives. Our expectations are based on fantasies, on illusions. Then we are surprised when the bubble bursts and the dream is shattered by stark truth.

The 3-D effect

Disillusionment tends to be the first step along a road paved with Ds! Disappointment, discouragement and despair soon follow unless we are strong, or fortunate enough to avoid them. And the problem is that once we start along that road, it is very hard to get off it, because the very nature of disillusionment makes you passive and too lethargic to do much to change your situation. We begin to allow life to dictate to us and end up 'OK, under the circumstances' when in truth we should be over them and not under them!

That word *disillusionment* is worth examining. The dictionary defines it as 'to wake up to reality, to have your eyes opened'. If we insist on living in unreality, then we should hardly be surprised when God uses circumstances to open our eyes and bring us back down to earth again. Yes, it hurts and it's easy to blame God and everybody else but ourselves when it happens. But in fact the fault lays fairly and squarely with us. We should not have built castles in the air in the first place. We should have taken a more sober assessment of various situations and based our hopes and expectations on something more realistic. That's why Paul encouraged the Roman Christians not to 'think of yourself more highly than you ought, but rather think of yourself with sober judgment' (Rom 12:3) and told the Galatians, 'If anyone thinks he is something when he is nothing, he deceives himself. Each one should test his own actions' (Gal 6:3–4). It's painful to do – but risky not to, for in the long run, it is more painful to live with illusions than it is with the truth. Illusions tend to be nice while they last but devastating when the bubble bursts. At least you know where you stand with the truth and you can build solidly and reliably upon it, like building a house on foundations of rock.

I once had to face the uncomfortable truth that God had not in fact called me to work as a full-time evangelist. This was after spending a largely fruitless six months being employed as one. I simply did not have the gifting, and far less the maturity for it. It was a desperately discouraging time, and the truth of my failings was almost unbearable to face. But at least afterwards I was able to start building on some truth. Better that than spend the rest of my life kidding myself and everybody else that I was an evangelist when I clearly was anything but.

A Wonderful Counsellor

Some people never recover from disillusionment when it affects them. It knocks them down and they never get up again. But disillusionment can be healed to the extent where we actually end up stronger than we were in the first place – even though we may be so low that we don't believe God can lift us up and perhaps don't particularly care whether he bothers or not.

For the God who sent Jesus to be a man of sorrows, acquainted with grief, also sent him in person to the dusty disillusionment of the Emmaus road to be a Wonderful Counsellor to two men whose worlds had been torn apart by the arrest, torture and execution of the man they thought would sort everything out. This Jesus is the one who not only understands the deep wounds that sear our spirits, but has experienced them himself and is equipped to do something about them, even when we are so discouraged that we aren't particularly interested in his help or anybody else's.

He is the one who managed to cope with the mixed emotions of seeing Judas fail to respond to the love and discipleship he had shown him for three years. He is the one who carried on after watching the rest of his disciples disappear when the going got tough in the Garden of Gethsemane that awful Passover night when treachery and wickedness abounded. He persevered when people in most of the places he visited rejected his message and when his family thought he was mad and urged him to come home – a frantic and emotional plea, perhaps, from a family worried that their reputation locally was about to be destroyed by their apparently wayward son. And he was still there when many of the people who shouted 'Hallelujah!' as he entered Jerusalem in triumph on Palm Sunday shouted 'Crucify him!' as he left it in tragedy just a few days later. Perhaps that was why he wept over Jerusalem, rather than bask in his popular acclaim? He knew what was coming next – that although he would enter that city covered in glory, he would leave it covered in blood. Yes, he knows all about disillusionment and failure – his life seemed to revolve around it. In one sense, the cross was his ultimate failure. And because of these experiences, he can help us cope with our 'down' times, even if we do sometimes think that he is the cause of them.

International rescue

God has a special rescue plan for anyone, anywhere whose hopes lie in a heap, whose dreams have died, whose visions have become void. Given time, he can eventually turn our situations around in the most surprising ways so that we can still inherit a future beyond our wildest dreams and enjoy a relationship with him that has a depth and an intimacy that can only be achieved through severe and even unfair testing.

And the wonderful thing about God is that he will come and help us whether we want it or not, or perhaps are not sure. Cleopas and his friend were certainly not looking for help on the road to Emmaus. (Quite the reverse, in fact – they were seemingly walking away from the other eleven disciples, who were sticking together during their difficulties and who were possibly the only people who could have helped them at that time.) Neither was Hagar. Neither was Jacob. Neither was David. Neither was Peter. But God's loving and sensitive nature will ensure that he will draw alongside us in the right way and at the right time, whether he is asked to or not. It's impossible to predict how he will do it, and we shouldn't try to. But we can be confident that he knows how to get behind our defences, to win our

friendship, to stir our hearts, to bring healing and wholeness and use whatever difficult circumstances we have
been through for our eventual good.

Making the first move

The fact that God often takes the initiative with disillusioned people should not encourage us just to sit
around, do nothing and wait for him to show. This would
be taking him for granted and abdicating our own responsibilities. We need to do our bit by calling on his name,
making decisions, seeking help and trying to stir our
hearts in the best way we know how. But undergirding
this is that we can trust God to make the first move on
those occasions when we're too low to do anything and
have gone beyond the point where we feel able or willing
to receive help. Any parent will testify to the fact that they
often reach out to help their children when, at first glance,
they do not appear to want it. Our heavenly Father is able
and willing to do the same, far more effectively.

He did it for a friend of mine. He went through a
terrible time of grief after his mother died, and in his
low state he committed adultery. One day he got so low
he walked out on his family – for good. But within a
matter of a week God had broken, unasked and unexpected, into his tormented world, bringing healing, forgiveness and reconciliation. Another chap I know became
desperately disillusioned after attempting to make the
grade as a minister following a stint at Bible college.
He failed completely and ended up a virtual vagrant,
with no job, no money, few possessions and just one
room to live in on his own. His sense of failure made

him cut himself off from God and other Christians
completely. But God eventually sent someone to find
him, again completely unasked, and within a matter of
a few years his life had been completely turned around.
He had a good job, owned a house, was married with a
child and had a valuable and satisfying teaching ministry
in a good church.

And what God did for him, he can do for you.

Note

1 The *UK Christian Handbook 1996–97*, produced by the Christian Research Association, showed that between 1980 and 1990,
2,900 new churches started – but 3,100 closed. And while
around 78,000 people joined churches after experiencing a
conversion (as opposed to transfer growth), the same number
left. The Handbook concludes that if current trends continue
the percentage of the population attending church will drop
from 10 per cent in 1989 to 8 per cent in 2015.

3

His Promises Are True . . . Aren't They?

There was a shuddering crash, followed by the sound of tinkling glass as my car hit a traffic island. 'That wasn't supposed to happen,' I thought to myself as I groped for my glasses. Well, one thing was for sure. God had not healed my eyesight! My car, and the precarious remains of a traffic island, more than proved the point. What had started as a great adventure in faith ended up with my 'no claims' bonus going straight out of the window, and with a large bill from the local council for a new traffic island dropping through my letter box a month later.

The Bible had been quite clear. 'Whatever you ask for in prayer, believe you have received it and it will be yours,' it said in Mark 11:24. So I prayed a simple prayer and asked God to heal my short-sightedness. Then I took off my glasses to prove that I really believed I had received the answer already. But then, from that point on, my faith and my experience headed off in rather different directions, with rather unfortunate results!

Did that mean that the Bible's promises were not true, and that God's word should not be trusted? Far from it! I think the problems lay more with me than with them. And after all, like many Christians, I had experienced too many occasions when God's word had proved to be true to ever entertain significant doubts about it. On one occasion I had glandular fever and was off work for weeks. Then I read the verse in Mark that led to the encounter with the traffic island, asked God to heal me, believed that he had done it and went off to work feeling grim . . . only to receive a complete and lasting healing later that day. On another occasion, my wife and I faithfully claimed God's promise that he would provide daily bread, and laid the table for tea at a time when our cupboards were completely bare. Thirty minutes later, somebody deposited two huge sacks of food on our doorstep, much to our relief and our children's, who were beginning to wonder just where their meal was coming from!

Yes, God's promises are true. But we would be kidding ourselves if we pretended that they *always* come true in our lives. On many occasions they do not. And when they don't, the let-down and disappointment can break our hearts, let alone a council traffic island! A friend of mine has still never come to terms with the fact that he believed with all his heart that God had given him a word that he would heal his sick mother – but she died. Another man I know gave up on God and church life altogether when he believed God would deliver him of alcoholism. He ended up back on the bottle.

So what do we believe? And how do we do it? How do we find the middle ground between religious, lifeless unbelief on the one hand and wild-eyed 'name it and claim it, blab it and grab it, confess it and possess it' faith teaching on the other? Here are some hints which can help us apply God's promises to our lives more reliably, and save us from some of the bitter disappointments that arise when those promises do not seem to be fulfilled.

1. What the Good Book says

Most Christians agree that the Bible is probably the most important tool that they possess. And yet precious few of us were taught how to read it properly when we first became Christians. I remember making important decisions by literally sticking pins into random pages of Scripture, and then wondering why things had not worked out too well!

Sadly, though, many of us continue in our Christian lives still not really understanding how to read Scripture reliably. Most of us do what Jesus' disciples and the two men on the Emmaus road did – we read the Scriptures *very* selectively and distort them with our mind-sets, preconceptions and tram-line theology.

The confusion that Jesus' followers suffered after his crucifixion was to some degree understandable. After all, Jews were taught from an early age that a Messiah would eventually come to bring salvation to his people and that he would emerge as a triumphant ruler of the nations. They had plenty of scriptures to support this belief. One of the first prophecies in the Bible concerning the Messiah is in Genesis 49:10 where he is clearly referred to as a conquering king: 'The sceptre will not depart from Judah, nor the ruler's staff from between his feet, until he comes to whom it belongs and the *obedience of the nations is his*' (my italics). The concept of a Messiah who will rule the nations runs consistently right through the Old Testament (Ps 110:1, 132:11; Is 2:4, 9:7, 11:10, 55:4; Jer 23:5; Dan 2:44, 7:14).

So Jesus' friends and disciples were not unreasonable in assuming that Jesus' ministry would involve him becoming a world ruler and putting the invading Romans to flight. They had probably clung to the teaching fervently ever since they were old enough to listen to the Scriptures being expounded by the rabbis in their local synagogues. During their three years' living and working with Jesus, they were no doubt eagerly anticipating the day when Jesus would fulfil their favourite scriptures and suddenly change, Superman-style, into an all-conquering hero who would take on and defeat the Romans. You can almost imagine them discussing among themselves when the Big Moment would arrive! And amazingly, they were still holding on to the idea *after* Jesus' death and resurrection. For one of the last things they said to Jesus before his ascension in Acts 1:6 was, 'Lord, are you at this time going to restore the kingdom to Israel?' They were still holding on stubbornly to their mistaken doctrine.

I imagine that Jesus was a touch frustrated when he answered them. Surely the eleven remaining disciples had got the message by now – that liberating Israel was not on his agenda at that time? He had told them enough times before. So his answer was bland and gave little away. 'It is not for you to know the times or dates the Father has set by his own authority,' he told them (Acts 1:7).

The problem the disciples had was that they had read

the Scriptures that suited them – and built their hopes
on them. The two men on the Emmaus road told Jesus
they had hoped he was the one who was going to
redeem Israel. But in doing so they ignored other
scriptures which stated quite clearly that Israel's
redemption was inseparably bound up with his second
coming (Lk 21:28).

That's why Jesus rebuked Cleopas and his friend and
said to them, 'How foolish you are, and how slow of heart
you are to believe all that the prophets have spoken. Did
not the Christ have to suffer these things and then enter
his glory?' The story in Luke 24 goes on to tell how
Jesus explained to those two disillusioned travellers
everything that the Scriptures said about the Messiah –
not just *some* of it. That's our problem. We are all too
quick to grasp some of what the Scriptures say about
something. But we don't take the time to find out *every-thing* they say. I'm sure if we read the verses in our Bibles
we don't underline, we'll begin to discover why the ones
we do underline never come to pass! This is why I am a
keen supporter of the Church of England's system of
having set scriptures to read each Sunday. At least that
way the congregation hears all of the Bible over a period
of time, and not just the leader's favourite passages.

In the case of these two men on the Emmaus road, I am
quite sure Jesus would have taken them right through the
Old Testament from the time of Moses, and shown them
the full tapestry of God's promises regarding the Messiah. He would have explained that while Isaiah had
prophesied that the Messiah would bring justice to the
nations (Is 42:1), he also said that the Messiah would be
despised and rejected, and that he would be pierced for

our transgressions and crushed for our iniquities just as he was on the cross. And he would have pointed out Isaiah's words: 'See, my servant will act wisely; he will be raised and lifted up and highly exalted. Just as there were many who were appalled at him – his appearance was so disfigured beyond that of any man and his form marred beyond human likeness' (Is 52:13–14). And he would have pointed out how Zechariah had prophesied that this Messiah would be gentle and ride on a donkey; and how David wrote of the Messiah:

> I am poured out like water, and all my bones are out of joint. My heart has turned to wax; it has melted away within me. My strength is dried up like a potsherd, and my tongue sticks to the roof of my mouth; you lay me in the dust of death. Dogs have surrounded me; a band of evil men has encircled me, they have pierced my hands and my feet. I can count all my bones; people stare and gloat over me. They divide my garments among them and cast lots for my clothing. (Ps 22:14–18)

He would have reminded them of his own predictions to the disciples: of how he had told them he would have to go to Jerusalem and suffer many things at the hands of the elders, chief priests and teachers of the law, and that he must be killed and raised up to life (Mk 10:33–34 and Lk 18:31–33). It was only after Jesus had opened these two men's eyes to all the Scriptures that they were able to see the whole picture. Then they would have understood that they had set themselves up for a crushing disappointment by misunderstanding the Scriptures.

Whenever we find that God's promises have apparently not come true, we need to ask ourselves, or someone else, whether we have grasped the whole truth of the issue from God's word. It's quite probable that we haven't. For instance, claiming God's promise that he will provide for all our needs (Phil 4:19) may not be effective if we have not paid our tithes in accordance with Malachi 3:10. Claiming that the devil will flee from us if we resist him (Jas 4:7) will not work if we have not obeyed the first half of this verse and submitted ourselves to God. And claiming the verse in 1 John 1:9 that we have been forgiven if we confess our sins will be pointless if we hold unforgiveness against someone else (Mk 11:25).

It is so important that we learn to read the Bible properly, and teach young Christians to do the same. We need to be like the Bereans, who examined the Scriptures every day (Acts 17:11). The Thompson chain reference Bible gives some timeless and extremely helpful advice about studying scriptures:

> Haphazard reading of a few verses of scripture every day is better than nothing, but it is not real Bible study. It is simply nibbling at the truth and does not tend to build up strong Christians. It becomes a new era in a believer's life when he forms the habit of going daily to the original sources of spiritual truth for his own personal nourishment. Most great truths do not lie on the surface. They must be brought up into the light by patient work.

We ignore advice like this at our peril.

2. Faith versus presumption

I once booked a holiday which I couldn't really afford, blithely confident that God would pick up the tab. After all, didn't Philippians 4:19 say that he would provide all

our needs? As you can probably imagine, God left me to
settle the bill, and I was saddled with a big debt for a
long time. He needed to teach me the hard way that
Scripture is not there to pick up and use to suit my
own purposes, no matter how noble they might seem.

So many Christians become disappointed about Bible
promises because they do as I did, and act on presumption rather than on faith. They see a situation, find a
verse to match it, and then assume that verse will come
true, just because it is in the Bible. Doing this leaves
God out of the equation. Before we can 'claim' a verse
to 'confess', we need to spend time discovering what
God is saying about that specific situation. For example,
it is easy to claim the verse 'It is not good for the man
to be alone' (Gen 2:18) when we are single and want to get
married. But what if God is asking us to remain single
(1 Cor 7:7)? We need to find out, since confessing God's
word is a waste of time unless we are in agreement with
him about it. The word 'confession' in Greek is the com-
bination of two words, *homos* (meaning 'same') and *logeo*
(meaning 'to say'). There is no point in presumptuously
confessing a promise from Scripture unless we are confident that we are saying the same about it as God is.

I often liken the Bible to a box of tools. All tools are
useful in their own way but they have to be used for the
right purpose and at the right time. A hammer is not
much help if you want to tighten a washer! Similarly,
when we are confronted by a situation, we need to ask
God to give us the right tool – or *rhema*, 'word' – for that
occasion, not go and find one that *we* think is appropriate.
God responds to faith, not presumption, and if we are not
in agreement with him over an issue, we can pray and fast

all we like. He does not change!

Once we have received the *rhema* ('word') for a situation, we need to remember to put our faith in Jesus, not in the word itself. After all, it is Jesus who is the author and finisher of our faith. Maintaining this perspective is essential, for it gives Jesus complete sovereignty in each situation – with the right to say 'No' to one of his own promises if he wants to. Unless we clearly understand this, we will hit disappointment time and time again.

3. Understanding God's timing

God is the only person who can be late and yet still be bang on time! And we can end up broken-hearted unless we grasp that his timing in fulfilling Bible promises is completely different from ours. He is not bound by time, and as Lord of time he can use it to suit his own purposes in ways that we cannot begin to imagine or understand.

Abraham had to wait most of his life before he began to see God's promise of fathering a nation come true. Why? Only God really knows.

Jesus had to wait thirty years before beginning to fulfil God's messianic promises for his life. Why? Only God really knows.

The Hebrew people had to endure slavery and oppression for 400 years before God raised up Moses to deliver them. Why? Only God really knows.

Martha and Mary had to wait several days before Jesus responded to their desperate plea to come and heal Lazarus. They must have endured terrible grief, torment and frustration during that time. Why? Only God really knows.

The disciples had to suffer hours of being buffeted

around by gales and waves when sailing home from the feeding of the 5,000 (Mt 14:13ff). Jesus did not walk on water to help them until the last watch of the night. He let them sweat it out for a few hours. Why? Only God really knows.

I have known countless situations when God appears to have left intervention hopelessly, even irredeemably late. It is only with hindsight I have been able to see that his timing was, in fact, perfect and that he was able to use the delay to do some useful work in teaching me patience and refining my character! So when God gives us a *rhema* or a promise for a situation, we need to leave the timing with him. He does know best! The chances are that he will leave things to the last minute. But when he does finally act to keep his word, he tends to do so very quickly, and with devastating effect.

4. Discerning God's plans

God's promises are inextricably linked to his plans for our lives. And not all of his promises apply to every Christian. That might sound hard, but it is true. For instance, in Psalm 90:10, Moses says that our lifespan is between seventy and eighty years. His wasn't! He lived to be 120, because God had other plans for him. And Jesus' certainly wasn't. He didn't even live to be half of seventy – again, God had other plans for him. And the same can be said about Jesus' disciples. Only John survived to see old age because, again, God had other plans for the others.

Similarly, in Deuteronomy 28:7 God clearly promises his people's enemies will be defeated. But the Old Testament is full of people who suffered bitter defeat at the hands of their enemies because of unresolved issues in their lives: Solomon, Achan, Saul, the list is endless.

We all have a responsibility to weigh God's promises against his plan for our lives. There is no point in claiming Psalm 2:8 that God will give you the nations for your inheritance if he is not planning to use you in an international ministry. That verse is true but it may never apply to you, even if you want it to. Similarly, you can confess Jeremiah 1:5, that God has called you to be a prophet to the nations, until you are blue in the face. But this verse will never come to pass in your life if God does not plan to use you in a prophetic ministry.

The body of Christ is so important in interpreting God's promises. There is tremendous safety in weighing up *rhema* with other Christians whom we trust and respect. Hopefully, they will put us right when we believe God is telling us through Psalm 150:3 to 'praise him with the sounding of the trumpet' by joining the church music group, although we haven't got a musical note in our body!

5. *Times and seasons*

There have been times in my life when my prayers have been answered easily and God's promises have come to pass almost straight away. But there have been other periods when the reverse is true. Why? Simply because, as Ecclesiastes chapter 3 reminds us, our lives are made up of seasons. And during the winter, things tend to be difficult: everything dies, there is no growth and few things bear fruit. We should all remember that our lives comprise a number of different seasons of varying lengths.

You can spot these seasons running right through Scripture. During Samuel's boyhood, 'the word of the Lord was rare' (1 Sam 3:1). Job had seasons in his life when things were wonderful and other times when they clearly were not. The same applied to Egypt in the time of Joseph – there were times of plenty and times of famine. There were 400 years of silence between the end of Malachi's ministry and the beginning of John the Baptist's – a long and difficult winter for God's people.

Christians often panic, become condemned and get very disillusioned during winter seasons, and mostly the problem is that they do not realise which season they are in. If they did, they would realise that the difficult time will be followed by spring – a time of warmth and rapid growth. When we are wanting to see God's promises fulfilled in our lives, we need to remember that they may be slower to come about in our autumns and winters than they are in our springs and summers.

6. A person, not a method

There is a mechanical element to the 'name it and claim it' approach to God's promises that bothers me. It leaves out our personal relationship with God and brings him down to the level of a chocolate machine: if you put the right money in, you get the right bar out.

Our problem is that we live in an instant society where it is possible to get virtually anything we want when we want it, whether it's cash from a dispenser or a loaf of bread from the corner shop at midnight. It is so easy to bring this attitude into our Christian lives and expect quick and easy fulfilment of every promise in the Bible. We need to avoid having our minds conformed to the world in this way, because God's dealings with us are often very slow and involve suffering and perseverance before we see a promise come to pass.

Treating God, or his word, like a chocolate machine is to my mind disrespectful. It forgets Paul's rebuke in Romans 9:20, 'But who are you, O man, to talk back to God?' It is also a certain route to disappointment. We should keep firmly in mind that behind every Bible promise is God himself, the promise-maker, who is Lord and who has the complete right to fulfil a promise to us – or to say no to it. I have promised my children pocket money every Saturday and a comic every Wednesday, but they soon discover that I have the discretion to withdraw both promises if their behaviour merits it! On other occasions I promise them things, but make them wait, since it is not good for them to grow up believing they can have what they want whenever they want it. The Prodigal Son is a good example of someone who received too much too soon. He received all his inheritance in one go and simply did not have the character to use it wisely. Similarly God may withhold a promise for us because we are not yet mature enough to cope with its fulfilment. We need to be walking closely with him to understand his dealings in our lives. He certainly won't give me the ministry of raising the dead at the moment, even if I claim it and have faith for it, because he knows only too well that I would become too proud if he used me in this way.

So now what?

Many of us have been left damaged and broken-hearted when God's promises have failed to come to pass, often in the most critical and painful situations. As a result, we find it hard to trust the Bible any more. This is completely understandable and God does not judge us or condemn us for it. But it is not a good place to stay! Each of us has a choice: to remain where we are, wallowing in our gloomy disappointment, or tentatively to move forward with God once again. It is not easy, for in some ways it is safer to stay put. At least if we never believe for anything again, we won't suffer any more disappointments. But for a believer, staying put will never be a place of real happiness, because deep down we will always know what we are missing by not moving on.

The best thing to do in this situation is, first, to analyse why the promise we put our faith in did not come true. The chances are the reason is contained somewhere in this chapter. If it is not, we should ask God to tell us – but remember, he may decide that it is better for us not to know for the time being.

Secondly, we need to do what I have recommended in this chapter and start reading the Bible again. It doesn't matter where! Your favourite book will do! Or you could choose the Psalms, which are full of people who endured the kinds of struggles that maybe you have endured. Going back to the Bible does not mean we have to start claiming great promises straight away. God is not in a hurry. But we can certainly begin reading it and, as we do so, we can begin renewing our friendship with Jesus once again. This is what happened to those two men on the Emmaus road. Their disappointment came from building false hopes on God's word. And so Jesus remedied the situation by taking them straight back to that word. Eventually it began to burn in their hearts again and that, in turn, brought recognition of who Jesus was. You too will find that if you go back to the word, it will come alive again, because it is living and active (Heb 4:12). Remember, too, the word of God is eternal. It will be the same in heaven as it is now, so it is best that we get used to it now, for we are going to have to live with it for ever!

4

Disappointed in Prayer

It was late at night and I was eager to get home after a
long church meeting. As I was leaving, a friend of mine
asked me to pray for his mother. It was a desperate
situation. She had been diagnosed as having terminal
cancer and had only been given a few months to live.

To be honest, I was tired and didn't really want to
pray. I just wanted to go home to bed. So I mumbled a
few rather faithless words, expected nothing to happen
– and was more surprised than anyone to hear later on
that the dear lady had recovered! I learned an important
lesson on that occasion: if God wants to heal someone,
or answer a prayer, then he will, despite us rather than
because of us.

More Christians become disillusioned through un-
answered prayer than through anything else. And the
problem is that often there does not seem to be any
rhyme or reason why some prayers are answered and
some are not.

A friend of mine was once asked to go and pray for a

woman who was dying in hospital of a brain tumour. The ward was dingy and crowded with visitors, most of whom were jostling for a better position to watch football on the television. The language was foul and the atmosphere completely godless. My friend prayed for the woman without much faith at all, but heard a week later that a brain scan had revealed the tumour had vanished. What made the incident even more strange was that the woman was not a Christian before she was healed and had no interest in becoming one afterwards, either. She made a full recovery, but never came through to the Lord.

Compare this with the many sick and suffering Christians who remain unhealed after trusting God faithfully for years and you start to realise that God's ways are certainly not ours! A missionary friend of mine went to work in a remote, Muslim area of Africa and prayed for more than forty years for the people there to be saved. During that time he did not see a single person become a Christian. People did, however, finally begin turning to God, but only when my friend had retired and returned home! He later remarked to me, 'Prayer is as big a mystery as the God we pray to!'

He had a good point. But if prayer was not like this, it would simply become an empty, mechanical method, devoid of any heart and relationship. Sometimes God surprises us with some astonishing answers to prayer and I am sure that we should all be seeing breakthroughs like this more often than we do. But the problem is that sometimes, he doesn't. And we need to be able to cope, and come to a place of peace, when those faith-filled prayers don't get answered, even though they are bulging with the *rhema* which was supposed to guarantee a quick and effective result.

As in all other aspects of our spiritual lives, it is important not to have wrong expectations from prayer. This can be difficult when, at the same time, we are meant to be exercising faith. We need to allow for all kinds of possibilities in our prayer lives. Doing so does not indicate a lack of faith. Quite the reverse: it indicates a mature faith which is based on all that Scripture says about prayer rather than just some of it. Quick and astonishing answers are wonderful, and we should yearn to see more of them. But they are only part of a tapestry of prayer which contains many other things besides.

So how do we avoid the crushing disappointments from unanswered prayers?

1. *Prayer is sometimes* meant *to be a struggle!*

If we expect instant answers to our prayers on every occasion, then disillusionment is guaranteed, because Scripture promises no such thing. God does, occasionally, give quick and quite miraculous answers. When the Israelites were complaining about the lack of drinking water at Marah (Ex 15:24), Moses cried out to the Lord and received an answer straight away. Elijah saw fire fall from heaven the moment he asked for it in 1 Kings 18:37–38. Not quite in the same league, but once, not long after I became a Christian, I prayed for a ticket to see my beloved Arsenal play the deadly enemy . . . not Satan, but Spurs. Incredibly, someone came and gave me a ticket for one of the best seats in the ground in less than five minutes! But answers like this are, I have found, the exception, not the rule. Most prayers take time to be answered. After all, Jesus prayed for all believers to be one in John 17:20–21, and is still waiting for it to happen, 2,000 years and many revivals later!

Scripture makes it clear that prayer is often a struggle – in fact Jesus went out of his way to stress the point. In the story of the unjust judge in Luke 18:1–8, Jesus drives home the importance of perseverance in prayer, a point he brings out again in Matthew 7:7–8, where he says, 'Ask and it will be given to you; seek and you will find; knock and the door will be opened to you.' Asking, seeking and knocking all take time and effort, and it is important that we see that most biblical references to 'perseverance' occur in the context of prayer.

Paul, too, takes up the theme in no uncertain terms. In his letter to the Thessalonians, he says that he has been praying earnestly for them night and day – that's what I call devotion (1 Thess 3:10). He urges the Colossians to *devote* themselves to prayer and to follow the example of a saint called Epaphras, who was always wrestling in prayer for them (Col 4:12). And he tells the Thessalonians to *pray continually* (1 Thess 5:17).

We should always approach prayer with the attitude that we may well be in for a long haul with many requests, and may have to face some struggles before the answers are given, especially when we are praying for things that the devil hates, such as the conversion of unsaved members of our family. This safeguards against disappointment. If, then, God surprises us by moving more quickly than hoped for then that is a bonus.

Many people ask, 'But *why* is prayer such a struggle?' I wish I knew! And I wish it wasn't. My personal theory is that prayer is God's way of training us and preparing us, not just for the rest of our lives on earth, but for eternity. He is developing our spiritual muscles, and like any exercise, this involves pressure and sweat! In the parable of the talents, Jesus makes it clear that some of us can look forward to ruling over up to ten cities when we get to heaven (Lk 19:11-27). But the people who are given this privilege will be the ones who have proved themselves faithful over small things on earth. I believe that prayer is one of those 'small things', and we cannot hope to enjoy a great position and inheritance in heaven if we have not proved ourselves faithful in this critical area on earth.

2. Praying in God's will

I have to confess that I did pray once that I would win the National Lottery, and was more concerned that week about six numbers than studying Bible passages like Numbers 6! And it came as no great surprise to me that some other lucky punter somewhere struck gold, whereas I just wasted £1.

I have no doubts that God heard my prayer. But he did not answer it, because I was certainly not praying in line with his will for my life. In 1 John 5:14 it says: 'This is the confidence we have in approaching God: that if we ask anything according to his will, he hears us.' The theologian B. F. Westcott takes up the point: 'True prayer – the prayer that must be answered – is the personal recognition and acceptance of the divine will.'

Looking back over my life, I can certainly say that the prayers that have not been answered have been the ones where I have prayed with selfish motives, or have misunderstood what God was seeking to achieve in a situation. I was once asked to join a group of people who wanted to pray for a man who had been seriously ill for a long time. I declined, simply because I wasn't sure that God wanted to heal him on this occasion. To pray for healing risked causing him even more disillusionment than he was suffering already if those prayers weren't answered. My opinion wasn't very popular although circumstances rather sadly proved it to be correct. God's will, for whatever reason, was that he would not be healed, or certainly not at that time.

3. Let God answer in his own way

A friend of mine once prayed that God would clear his debts. God certainly did! Within a year, my friend was declared bankrupt and all his debts were wiped out. However, bankruptcy was the last thing he wanted, and when it was imminent he prayed that he would avoid it. But that was God's solution to the situation. In this, my friend discovered that some prayers are not answered in the way we expect! And we shouldn't be surprised, since God does promise us in Isaiah 55:8 that his ways are not ours. That means that when we think he should answer in one way, he will probably do it in another . . . not to be awkward, but because he is wiser than we are and sees a bigger picture than we do. And he always has our best interests at heart.

Letting God do things his way sometimes means accepting that he will exercise his royal prerogative and simply say 'No' – which he, as Lord, is fully entitled to do, without our permission or consent! And looking back over the years, I can honestly say I am grateful for some of God's 'Nos'. They might have been hard to bear at the time, but a 'Yes' would have been even harder to bear in the long run. I remember once praying that God would use me as a missionary in Africa. In hindsight, I think both the Africans and I have every reason to be glad that God said 'No'!

4. Watch for blockages

The Bible contains a long and rather uncomfortable list of things which will block answers to prayer. Whenever I read it I usually find that I am guilty of at least one of them! And if we have a blockage, no amount of prayer and fasting and crying out to God will see our prayers answered. Removing, or dealing with the blockage, is the only way out. Here are some of them:

>   Disobedience (Deut 1:43–46)
>   Secret sin (Ps 66:18)
>   Indifference (Prov 1:24–28)
>   Neglecting the poor (Prov 21:13)
>   Iniquity and sin (Is 59:2)
>   Stubbornness (Zech 7:11–13)
>   Instability (Jas 1:6–7)
>   Not bothering to ask (Jas 4:2)
>   Asking with the wrong motives (Jas 4:3)
>   Husbands not respecting their wives (1 Pet 3:7)

If we don't deal with issues like these when they arise, then we can be certain that our prayers will go un-answered . . . and continuing heartbreak will follow.

Heartbreaks over healing

Healing is certainly one of God's greatest mysteries. As Ronald Dunn says in his book *Will God Heal Me?* (Kingsway 1997): 'It's easy to philosophise about suffering when you're not doing any. But when the beast crouches at your own door, it's another ball-game – the answers don't come as easily then.'

I tend to be a bit like that – I can dazzle you all day with God's promises about healing, until I wake up with a sore throat. Then things are different. Many Christians become bitterly hurt because God has not healed people when they expected him to. I am one of them. Maybe you are too. I thought he would heal my father when he was dying of cancer. He didn't. I thought he would heal my best mate when he was dying from a brain tumour at the age of fifteen. He didn't. Having said this, it's easy to become gloomy and despondent. We should remember that there are many occasions when God does heal. He healed me of a chronic and life-threatening back condition. He healed my deformed jaw and the arthritis which was crippling both of my hands. And over my years as a Christian I have seen him cure everything from corns to cancer.

And this is the problem. Sometimes God heals, sometimes he doesn't, and we poor humans find it hard to know when he will and when he won't! I am sure that if we knew categorically that God was not going to heal someone, the pain of disappointment would be far easier to bear. Sometimes, of course, he will tell us, if we take the time and trouble to ask him. Our difficulty is that sometimes we are so full of 'faith' that we are not prepared to allow for the possibility that anything other than healing will take place.

Here are some further thoughts about healing which I have found helpful:

1. Who is Lord?

A pastor I know once said, 'When a non-Christian is sick, *God* proves he is Lord. When a Christian is sick, *you* prove he is Lord.' In other words, if we find that God is quicker to heal a non-Christian than he is a Christian, this is because his main purpose in healing is not just to get us better. He is also looking at what eternal good he can bring from each situation. So if healing non-Christians means that they will become Christians as a result, then God may well heal them, if their hearts are ready for it, since that seals their souls for eternity. And if, by withholding healing from a Christian, he can get them to address an issue in their life, or refine their characters in a particular way, then again, eternal good will have been done.

It is easy for us to say that Jesus is Lord when everything is fine. But when we are ill we find out how much we mean it. Lordship means just that. And if Jesus is really our Lord, then we must be prepared to let him leave us unhealed or even let him take our lives, for reasons best known to himself. After all, at the end of the day, death is the most complete form of healing a Christian can ever receive!

2. Areas of responsibility

Ultimately, healing is God's responsibility, not ours. But we still have our part to play. In Mark 16:18 Jesus said,

'They [believers] will place their hands on sick people, and they will get well.' Our responsibility, as believers, is to place our hands on the sick. The rest is down to God. We cannot swap roles with him. Similarly, in James 5:15 we are told, 'And the prayer offered in faith will make the sick person well; the Lord will raise him up.' Our part is to pray – God's is to heal. Ultimately, all we can do is be diligent in carrying out our duties and leave the rest to God. This keeps things in their right place. With any supernatural work of God, we need to remember that it is God who is 'super' – and we who are 'natural'. If we try to reverse those roles, problems and disappointments will undoubtedly arise.

I remember once being stricken with guilt when a man died after I had prayed with him for healing. A friend of mine had to remind me that God was his healer, not me.

3. Be wise with your words

I have come across repeated situations when well-meaning Christians tell those people tending dying friends and relatives, 'This sickness will not end in death.' Very scriptural – Jesus said the words to his disciples when he heard about Lazarus' illness in John 11:4. But then the person dies, leaving a bereaved family not just with grief to cope with, but with guilt and a feeling of disillusionment towards God as well. We need to have enough common sense to realise that some sicknesses *do* end in death – after all, we all die one day, usually when we get old! Even Lazarus went to glory eventually, after being raised from the dead! To prophesy healing to the old and terminally ill can rob both the person and their families of the chance to handle their death with peace and dignity. I have known people torn apart by the fact that they never said goodbye to their loved ones because they were caught up with the unrealistic notion that they would be healed right up to the time they died. How terrible. No wonder the surviving relatives become disillusioned and give up. I have seen friends try to put families back together after the death of a relative whom God was expected to heal. At times like these I would like to get hold of the people who spoke those words and draw their attention to the Old Testament instruction to stone prophets whose words did not come to pass! The trouble is, they never seem to be around to help clear up the mess. We should not be afraid to teach people to die well as well as to live well. We are very good at the latter but don't always address the former.

Victims of war

The church has woken up to spiritual warfare in a wonderful way over the last ten years. And it does work! I used to attend a church in London where we saw some wonderful breakthroughs after spiritual battles, not just in the lives of individuals, but in some geographical areas too. We saw the crime rate fall, we saw an alleyway which had been the haunt of muggers become safe, we saw situations of unrighteousness exposed and we saw the lordship of Jesus awesomely demonstrated over other beliefs.

But we also saw some crushing failures and situations where warfare didn't seem to work. We saw some very good people become victims of Satan's counter-attacks. And some of us felt like giving up at times. So we all need to know how to handle both successes and failures. We must learn how to cope when, after years of spiritual warfare and evangelism, the enemy still appears to be out-manoeuvring us most of the time and increasing his sphere of influence, while our victories seem as rare as the England cricket team's.

We also need to remember when we 'struggle against rulers, authorities, powers of this dark world and spiritual forces of evil' (Eph 6:12) that, as in a wrestling match, the winner sometimes gets hurt along the way and the outcome is by no means certain. For even though Jesus won a complete victory over Satan through his sinless life, his death and his resurrection, that doesn't necessarily guarantee that we will be successful in enforcing that victory on every occasion. Jesus might be invincible – but we are certainly not, and our humanity, lack of faith, lack of knowledge of his word and our immaturity will often let us down and lead to our defeat in this hand-to-hand combat with the enemy. We ignore at our peril the warning in Revelation 13:7 about an end-times enemy who 'was given power to make war against the saints and to *conquer them*'. Yes, Jesus is the conqueror, and yes, he is infallible. But we are neither, and if we see ourselves differently, then we're basically putting ourselves on the same level as him and expecting to do better in life than every single hero of Scripture. Abraham, Moses, David, Elijah, Paul ... they all had their failings and their failures – and so will we.

As for Paul, we would all agree that he knew enough about spiritual warfare to wage it regularly and to write an illuminating chapter about it to the Ephesians. But even he was forced to admit that Satan had stopped him from getting to see the Thessalonians (1 Thess 2:18). If he suffered his setbacks and his defeats – and, as we saw earlier, in 2 Corinthians you'll find that he endured plenty of both – then so will we.

There is a lack of cautiousness about spiritual warfare which sometimes bothers me. People literally rush in where angels fear to tread. We should remind ourselves that even Jesus never tackled the powers and principalities while he was on earth. Warfare should always be left to soldiers – those who have been selected, trained, prepared, equipped and who are fit and ready for action. People who enter battles without the proper training and qualifications are likely to be the first on the casualty list.

So again, as in our approach to Bible promises, prayer and healing, we need to have a realistic understanding of what we can achieve. To do otherwise can result in us suffering from war wounds. We also need to ensure we are properly equipped before going into battle, by addressing the following points:

1. We should have victory over the enemy in our own life. If we haven't, we cannot possibly expect to bring victory into somebody else's.
2. We need to be submitted to God in every area of our lives.
3. Our sin should be confessed and repented of.
4. We should be firmly rooted and established in a local church. God wants soldiers, not a bunch of Lone Rangers. Even the Lone Ranger had Tonto!
5. We should be filled with the Holy Spirit, since he will give us the weapons we need to wage warfare.

6. We need to stay within our faith and the boundaries of our experience. To do otherwise is presumption, and is dangerous.

7. We need to be confident of our authority in Jesus, since without it we will face the devil on our own, and will lose.

Sounding off

When we are hurt or discouraged, it is so important that we learn how to get things off our chest.

When Jesus asked Cleopas and his friend on the Emmaus road what had been happening in Jerusalem recently, he certainly knew the answer better than anybody – after all, he had experienced it at first hand! But by asking them the question, he uncorked a waterfall. Out it all came ... a torrent of facts peppered with their disappointments, confusion and unanswered questions. It seems as though the two men scarcely paused for breath as they poured out their reply. Perhaps there was a twinkle in Jesus' eye as he listened to them, and maybe he was itching to tell them who he really was.

If we are going to find healing from disillusionment, there has to come a time when we sound off – to God. Some people find it is helpful to go through this process with another person, and while this can occasionally be valuable, it often merely taints the person we choose to speak to, and does not leave us feeling much different for very long. But whether we speak to someone else or not, it is still vitally important that we tell God exactly how we feel. He is ultimately the only one who really needs to hear it and who can do something about how we feel.

I'm not talking about going to him for a brief, daily grumble about our dreadful lot in life. This does not really achieve anything – quite the reverse, in fact, for grumbling and complaining will always keep God's people out of the Promised Land. We need to go further than a 'poor me' moaning session. We need to find time to be alone with God for a while without interruption, when we can tell him everything we think and everything we feel. We need to tell him where we believe he, or others, have let us down. We need to voice our frustrations, our hurts, our anger and any other emotions that we may have lurking around. The process needs to involve a real baring of our hearts, without any pretence and with nothing held back. God will not be shocked by anything we say to him!

I have done this two or three times during my Christian life, and the results have always been positive – life-changing, in fact. The process ensured that there was nothing obstructing my friendship and relationship with God any longer. It cleared the decks and enabled God to start reconstructing my present and my future, bringing correction and healing where necessary. And it enabled me to release the things in my heart to the person who knew me more intimately than anyone else on earth or in heaven. After all, Psalm 139:13 reminds us that it was God himself who created our inmost beings, and he is the only one who can effectively restore them.

David found enormous comfort from sounding off to God. In 1 Samuel 24:1ff he found himself, once again, on the run from the mad and jealous King Saul. The king had just returned from pursuing the Philistines and received word that David was in the desert of En Gedi.

So he mustered 3,000 of his best soldiers and set off in pursuit. They arrived at a place called the Crags of the Wild Goats and Saul went into a cave to relieve himself, not realising that David and his fighting men were holed up inside. David resisted the tempting suggestions from his men to do everyone a favour and finish Saul off once and for all while they had the chance, and instead satisfied himself by rather cheekily cutting a corner of the king's robe. But afterwards David was conscience-stricken as he realised the implications of what he had done and ended up in a state of confusion, guilt and frustration over the whole issue. He, like us, found it hard going to apologise to someone who really ought to be apologising himself!

Later on, David wrote Psalm 142 about the whole incident, and in verse 2 we read, 'I pour out my complaint before him; before him I tell my trouble.' The Hebrew word for 'pour' here is *shaphak*, which means to spill forth, or bare one's soul in tears. And the Hebrew word for 'complaint' is *siach*, which in this context means to talk disparagingly or, in other words, to have a good moan. So we can see that David was really pouring out some deep anger and hurt towards God about the difficult ongoing situation regarding Saul.

Long-suffering Job also found it helpful, and indeed essential, to bring his complaints before God. He discovered, as we no doubt will, that complaining to people does not achieve a great deal. And so we find him saying: 'I will not keep silent; I will speak out in the anguish of my spirit, I will complain in the bitterness of my soul' (Job 7:11). He certainly had good reason to do so! Complaining to God can be our salvation – or at least a helpful part of it.

Obviously such a conversation needs to be kept in perspective. At the end of the day, sounding off to God is not our right. It is an enormous privilege, a reflection of his grace and mercy. We should always remember that if it wasn't for Jesus, we would not be able to approach him or speak to him at all. I always feel uneasy when I hear people being too familiar and matey with God. Our friendship with him should have awe and respect at the heart of it. But we should nonetheless accept the privilege he generously gives us to complain to him – and make the most of it.

We should bear in mind, though, that David did not write two Psalm 142s! In other words, we do not find him having another moan about the same problems a few psalms later. If we complain and off-load our burdens to God, we should then leave them with him, for ever, and not keep on going over things in our hearts, or with him, or other people. Gene Edwards in his book *Letters to a Devastated Christian* (Tyndale) advises that once we have made our complaints, we should vow never to speak about them again. I am learning that there is enormous healing to be found by doing this, although it is very difficult to keep quiet about things which have left us hurt and damaged. It needs a great deal of personal discipline and self-control, exercised over a long period, to learn to stop reciting our tale of woe to everybody we meet. We should remember that it achieves nothing for us and probably bores them stiff!

Selwyn Hughes, of Crusade for World Revival, tells the story of a woman he knew who was suffering terrible disillusionment. She told him, 'I used to pray, but had never thought of actually surrendering my discouragement into the hands of Christ and leaving it there. I did just that and he touched my life in a way I never thought possible.'

There is a lesson there for all of us! Cleopas and his friend found that it worked. And so will we.

Groups and rumours of groups

When Cleopas and his friend became disillusioned, they got together and off they went. And it has to be said that their journey and conversations got them precisely nowhere, until Jesus intervened. They were just as disillusioned after they shared their hearts with one another as they were before.

Disillusionment is cunning. For while on the one hand disillusioned people want to be alone, on the other it doesn't take them long to find an ally. Disillusioned people often have an uncanny ability to find one another, even in a crowded meeting, and they cling on to one another for mutual support. There is nothing necessarily wrong with this, although I have found that this kind of support rarely achieves anything positive, unless Jesus is actively involved, as he was on the Emmaus road. Instead what often happens is that you end up with a 'them and us' situation. 'Us' are the disillusioned people who are hurt and misunderstood – and 'them' are everybody else, and especially the leaders, who would not possibly understand how they felt and perhaps were the cause of the hurt in the first place. Before you know it, you have a group within a group – and this is something that Jesus will never bless, because he never blesses disunity or criticism.

If you get involved with other disillusioned people, you tend to end up worse than you were in the first place. You get dragged down by their problems as well as your own and with a worse set of negative attitudes thrown in! If we are in such a group, we need to take care. For even though we are despondent and in pain, finding a gang of like-minded grumblers will only intensify the situation and give ground for sin too – gossip, criticism, and division. And these things inevitably put even more obstacles in the way of getting back to a good place with God. If we are going through a bad time, it is better to go through it alone, or with someone who is strong, rather than to drag others down with us or mix with those who make things worse.

5

Helping Ourselves

I knelt weeping beside my father's hospital bed and watched helplessly as his life ebbed away, his body racked with cancer. He had become ill, right out of the blue. One day he seemed to be very healthy for a man of his age. The next he suddenly became desperately ill and, after some tests, the doctors said that he didn't have very long to live. I loved him and I desperately wanted him to survive, especially as I was getting married the following year and was eager for him to be part of the celebrations.

Some friends and I began to pray for his healing, boldly and faithfully. The more we prayed, the more confident we became that God was going to perform a miracle and heal him. We had prophecies and words from the Lord to reinforce our belief. We were convinced that it was simply a matter of time before he'd be healed. We knew plenty of Bible verses about healing and we thought we had the faith for it.

But he died, painfully and terribly, with me next to him, wondering where God was and indeed if he actually

existed. And although the grief and pain of losing the dad
I adored was almost too deep to bear at times, the disillusionment with the God who didn't answer my prayers,
and who appeared to change his plans at the last minute,
cut deeper and lasted longer. I cried until I had no tears
left. The struggle went on for a long, long time and I
carried the terrible burden of responsibility . . . that his
death was my fault, and that if I had prayed the right
prayer, then dad would have been healed.

As a result, for many years afterwards I struggled to
find faith when it came to praying for other sick people to
get better. Every time I laid hands on them, a voice would
whisper in my ear, 'What makes you think God will heal
them? He didn't heal your dad! He let you down, didn't
he? You can't rely on him. And anyway, *your* prayers don't
work. You know they don't. They didn't then and they
won't now.' My lack of faith led to more disappointments.
That led to condemnation, and the disillusionment that
followed was traumatic and intense. My ministry started
to recede instead of grow. Strong relationships went
wrong and many of my closest friends suddenly disappeared. There were disappointments and setbacks in
church, in my job, in my ministry – everywhere! God's
promises for my life seemed to vanish like manna in the
wilderness. They were gone, seemingly for ever – and I
didn't really care.

As we saw at the beginning of this book, deferred hope
was the cause. I had hoped, wrongly, for a healing that
God had not promised, and then could not begin to face
the bitter consequences. As a result, I almost ended up
with virtually no faith at all. It was an awful, desperate
time. The disillusionment completely swamped me until

I had no motivation, no dreams, no hopes and no prayers left. I sank lower than I thought it possible to ever sink. I lost my zeal; God's word was cold and uninspiring; I didn't want to pray, and the heavens seemed locked and bolted when I did. I couldn't see any point in getting help or in going to church meetings any more. People tried their best to help, but without success – yet I was a leader in a church during the whole of this period!

And yet through those years of pain, God's gentle, waterfall-like voice began to whisper: 'Will you still love me, even when your heart's broken and when I haven't done what you expected me to do?'

I wasn't sure of my answer for a long time then and sometimes I still hesitate to give it even now. How on earth could I love a God who appeared to specialise in *not* answering my prayers and *not* doing the things I had faithfully asked him to do – and which his word appeared to say he *would* do?

This valley of disillusionment caught me completely by surprise, at a time when things were going well. My walk with God was fairly stable, my prayer life was quite strong, Jesus was very real to me and was beginning to use me in some situations. The present was good and the future was exciting. Then came a sudden knock and everything seemed to fall apart. The recovery process was slow and painful, and indeed is still continuing to this day. And in a sense, you never recover completely from serious knocks like bereavement. The pain diminishes and you get used to it. But the scars are still there and this is not necessarily wrong, if we can allow God to use them for his glory. However, we need to be prepared to help ourselves if we can.

Sharing in Jesus' sufferings

Jesus was the greatest example we will ever have of how
to live a victorious life. He triumphed every time,
whether it was over demons, Pharisees, the wind and
waves, empty wine jars or incurable sicknesses. He was
always on top, until, of course, he was crucified. And that
defeat only happened because he chose to allow it.

But it is easy to ignore the fact that Jesus' victorious
lifestyle was accompanied by terrible pain ... pain
inflicted by his family who thought he was mad, from
his countrymen who rejected him, by people he healed
who then ignored his advice, from his disciples who fled
when the going got tough, and by God himself when he
rejected him on the cross. Whenever you see victory in
Jesus' life, you will normally find pain right alongside it
somewhere, a fact which books on 'victorious Christian
living' tend to miss out.

Most Christians tend to opt for one aspect of Jesus'
lifestyle or the other – either for victory or for suffering.
You do not meet many people who embrace both in the
way Jesus did. But, as Paul says, 'The sufferings of Christ
flow over into our lives' (2 Cor 1:5). That's the way it
should be, and if we expect anything different, we will
end up disappointed. This is why Paul wrote to the
Philippians, 'I want to know Christ and the power of
his resurrection and the fellowship of sharing in his
sufferings' (Phil 3:10). Paul wanted both the power and
the suffering. And that's what he got!

Many Christians use this verse as a reason to put up
with a lot of things that Jesus never suffered! He never
suffered sickness. He never suffered the consequences of

his own sin. These things need to be avoided, not embraced as being something spiritual. But if we are really determined to follow Jesus we can certainly expect to experience the rejection, let-downs, persecution, ridicule and temptations, attacks by the enemy and the disappointments that he endured. As Paul found, the knowledge that we are joining him in something that he suffered will produce a bond with him that nothing and nobody can break.

How do we cope with suffering?

If we don't master suffering, it will master us and we will become so hurt and disillusioned that we risk losing our faith altogether. None of us should be so confident as to think that this could never happen to us! It could. We are all vulnerable.

Jesus, Peter and Paul, and the other apostles somehow managed to find joy and peace in the face of suffering. Jesus was full of compassion and forgiveness as he hung in agony on the cross. Peter was peaceful enough to go to sleep in the heavily guarded squalor of a Roman jail, knowing full well he probably faced execution the following day. And Paul and Silas managed to sing hymns and pray in similar circumstances – and that was after being severely flogged. How did they manage it? How did they avoid becoming negative and depressed? And how can we help ourselves during difficult trials?

1. Get things in perspective

I once told a friend of mine about a difficult time I was having, and he simply laughed and said, 'You're lucky.

You could be dying of hunger in the Third World.' He was right.

This is not meant to minimise some of the genuine struggles that we all go through from time to time. But we should keep them in perspective, and that means keeping God at the centre of our suffering. This can be hard! I often find that he is the last person I want to talk to when I am low. But we should always focus on the fact that God's love and goodness will always be greater, and last longer, than anything else we may be going through. The psalmist Asaph found this in Psalm 73:21–24 – a psalm which gives us a very helpful insight into how to cope with life's trials. Asaph spends the first 22 verses bemoaning his lot and voicing some real struggles he was having with his faith. 'When my heart was grieved and my spirit embittered, I was senseless and ignorant; I was a brute beast before you,' he says. But then, in verse 23, his attitude changes. He somehow manages to find God in it all and begins to see things from the right perspective. That is why he is able to say, 'Yet I am always with you; you hold me by my right hand. You guide me with your counsel, and afterwards you will take me into glory.' By God's grace, we will be able to do the same – able to say 'Yet . . .' amid the most desperate and unjust situations, and realise that God has always been there with us, guiding us, leading us by the hand and taking us into his glory.

2. *Allow suffering to purify us*

I always chuckle when we sing the chorus that goes, 'Purify my heart . . . as gold, pure gold,' because what in effect we are saying to God is, 'Turn the heat up,

Father. Send some suffering!' Maybe if we thought through the implications of this song, we would not be so quick to sing it!

Yet this is what suffering does. It purifies us in the way that silver and gold are purified by intense heat in the furnace (Ps 66:10; 1 Pet 1:7). If we can keep this in mind, it will help us to see that trials and difficulties are for a purpose.

3. Accept correction

My children will tell you that correction by their father sometimes hurts! And so does correction by our heavenly Father. Hebrews 12:7 says, 'Endure hardship as discipline; God is treating you as sons.' When suffering comes to our lives, we need to examine our hearts and our lives and see which areas God is seeking to correct. It might be painful, but it will be worth it! As Psalm 119:67 says, 'Before I was afflicted, I went astray, but now I obey your word.' God will often use suffering to discipline us. I remember meeting a man who had been sick for many months. 'God's teaching me something,' he explained when I asked him whether he had asked God to heal him. 'You must be a slow learner, then,' I said. The quicker we learn the lesson, the sooner the suffering stops!

4. Enter God's kingdom!

We hear a lot about God's kingdom in church nowadays. But sometimes people miss out one of the key entry requirements. Paul and Barnabas set it out clearly to the disciples in churches they had planted in Lystra, Iconium and Antioch. 'We must go through many hardships to enter the kingdom of God,' they said (Acts 14:22). In other words, there's no easy way in.

That word 'hardships' is worth examining. The Greek is *thlipsis* and means 'to break, to crush, press, compress, squeeze . . . grievous affliction or distress . . . pressure or burden upon the spirit'. If you are experiencing some of these things, then be encouraged! God is getting you into his kingdom. It's a bit like queuing up to get into a football match! Yes, you'll be broken, crushed, compressed and squeezed as you go through the turnstile. But once in, you will be glad you got there.

5. *Wait for the good times . . .*

I once got furious when people quoted Romans 8:28 at me when I was going through a difficult time. 'In all things God works for the good of those who love him,' they would say. The problem was that at the time, I wasn't really sure if I did love him any more and whether, therefore, the verse still applied to me!

Another chap got the rough end of my tongue once when he assured me during a really difficult time, 'You'll look back and laugh at it all in a few years from now!' He might have been right, but it didn't seem much help at the time!

It can sound very glib to trot out verses and statements like these to people who are suffering. But glib or not, they are true and we need to try and hang on to them. No matter what you are going through now, God *is* working for your good. You may not understand how or why, but he is – providing you give him time. Sadly, some things cannot be rushed. But Paul was confident, and so am I, that you will be able to look back one day, see the good that eventually came from your difficulties . . . and perhaps even laugh about them.

6. Recognise where the trouble came from

We will never come through a time of suffering unless we are clear about one thing – that God personally allowed it, unless, of course, we have brought it on ourselves in some way. Scripture is quite clear about this. 'When disaster comes to a city, has not the Lord caused it?' asked Amos (3:6). Isaiah reiterates the point (45:7), 'I bring prosperity and create disaster; I, the Lord, do all these things.'

Because of this we need to try and look beyond our suffering and see God's hand at work in our lives and circumstances. Many people try and put every trial and knock-back down to the devil. Some of them seem to receive far more attacks than Jesus ever did! Even he had a break from Satan for a while (Lk 4:13). But as Job 1:8 and Luke 22:31 confirm, even Satan himself can only trouble us or sift us if he has obtained God's permission first.

If we can see that God has allowed suffering to come, then we will understand that 'My grace is sufficient for you, for my power is made perfect in weakness' (2 Cor 12:9). In other words, God will always give us the grace and whatever else we need, to get through difficult circumstances which he has personally sanctioned.

Be real about how you feel!

This is an important key to helping ourselves during difficult times.

I remember being greeted at a church door once during a time when I was going through a desperate struggle as a new Christian. It was one of those churches where you were expected to feel fine all the time and smile inanely in all circumstances.

'How are you, brother?' asked the beaming welcomer, who, on reflection, was probably just as low as I was but far more experienced at disguising it.

'Awful,' I mumbled.

'Ah,' he said, his beam frozen to his face as he struggled to cope with this rather unexpected and unscripted response. 'Well,' he ventured, wondering what to say next. 'Praise the Lord!'

He might have wanted to but, rightly or wrongly, I certainly didn't.

Christians often have trouble being honest when they are downcast, sad or morose. Our theology – and other people – present us with problems. To admit that we are low implies that there is something wrong with our relationship with God, that we are lacking in faith, or that our prayers are not being answered for some reason. The thinking goes that if we were right with God, then we would be gloriously positive and happy in every and any situation. And since the Holy Spirit has filled us with the fruit of joy, then to be anything other than joyful is tantamount to serious spiritual failure.

As a result of this thinking, many Christians become dishonest or they cover up their hurts, problems and sins because mentioning them is seen as negative or somehow lacking in faith. The fact that God wants us to be honest about how we feel both to him and to other people sometimes gets lost amid a lot of super-spiritual idealism and the fear that voicing anything remotely negative is somehow being critical.

Another problem is that we are taught to praise God in all circumstances. Now this is right – Scripture says so. David told Araunah in 1 Chronicles 21:24 that he would not sacrifice to God that which cost him nothing. And in Psalm 35:28 we are encouraged to have praises on our lips all day long. But in doing so we can again end up disguising our real feelings: we smile and say 'Hallelujah' through gritted teeth when in reality we are dying inside. Now this is not wrong. Far from it. We need to learn to praise the Lord amid adversity. But we also need to be completely honest about our feelings both to God and our friends. It is possible to do both at once without being some spiritual schizophrenic. As we saw in the previous chapter, it is not a sin to have a good moan to God. Many psalms bear witness to David's ability to say exactly how he felt while still wearing the garment of praise.

Admitting how we feel can be even more difficult in our hectic twentieth-century churches where people are too busy establishing God's kingdom to spend time caring for others. Churches which focus heavily on evangelism are sometimes weak on pastoral care. When people ask us how we are and we say, 'Lousy,' we can almost feel them flinch as they begin to think, 'Oh dear. If I ask why, this conversation is going to last at least five minutes which means I won't have time to deliver fifteen agendas for tomorrow night's pastoral team meeting.' So the pressure is on us to say, 'Yes, I'm fine,' in order to avoid wasting busy people's time.

I have lost count of the number of sad people I meet in churches. And the problem is that they usually don't show it, for all the reasons we've just examined. Instead they cover it up with a fake grin and a 'Fine – I'm a child of God. How could I be anything else?' response to your questions about their welfare.

I remember talking to a friend about his father-in-law, who also attended our church. My friend told me, 'He's got to be the happiest person I know. You simply never see him without a smile on his face.'

My friend was surprised when I told him, 'Actually, I think he's the saddest. The smiles are just a cover-up of how he really feels.'

The truth came out when I prayed for his father-in-law a few weeks later. God released that sadness amid tears that flowed and, as time went by, that smile became genuine. At last, God had penetrated the well-rehearsed cover-up.

We need to develop the ability to discern how people are *really* feeling. We are told in Mark 2:8 that Jesus knew what was in people's hearts, and there are several other occasions (Mt 12:25, 22:18; Lk 6:8, 11:17; Jn 2:25) where he apparently knew what people were thinking. We too need to ask the Holy Spirit for discernment and insight so that we can do the same – not to be mystical or engage in mind-reading, and certainly not to pry, but to be able to love people in a way that reaches the real them, rather than the superficial top coat that they wear to church meetings. If we allow the Holy Spirit to show us their wounds, their hurts and their raw emotions, then we can at least be sensitive to them, and perhaps help them if God tells us to.

Many people are walking wounded these days and my

prayer is that our churches will become safe and secure enough for them to express their pain so that God can heal them. If people can't feel safe in church, then where can they? I remember feeling terrified in church when I was a child. The vicar was remote, solemn and dressed in frightening robes. Everyone seemed serious and frowned at me if I even dared to move. The smell of incense made me feel sick. All I wanted to do was go home. And the sad thing is that I still sometimes meet children nowadays who say the same – even in newer churches. They find it scary when adults start speaking in tongues, falling over unconscious, screaming, laughing or shrieking. If one of my children started behaving like that at home, I'd send him to his room. But I expect them to remain unmoved if I, or other people, start doing it in church.

Back on the Emmaus road, there were no super-spiritual cover-ups for Cleopas and his friend. They were browned off and it showed. The New International Version describes the look on these two disciples' faces as 'downcast' – sad, rueful or morose. It is the same word that is used in 2 Corinthians 7:6 when a seriously disillusioned Paul told the Corinthians, 'But God, who comforts the *downcast*, comforted us by the coming of Titus' (my italics). In other words, God healed Paul's disillusion-ment by drawing Titus alongside him, in exactly the same way that he had healed Cleopas and his friend by bringing Jesus alongside them years earlier. And it is similar to the word used in Psalm 42:5 where the sons of Korah lamented, 'My soul is downcast within me,' as they went through a bitter time of disillusionment.

The Authorised Version, however, uses the Greek word *skuthropos*, which means 'scowling face' to describe

Cleopas and his friend – an old-fashioned way of saying that they were completely naffed off! We stiff and starchy Britons are not as honest as these two men were about expressing our real feelings. Becoming honest about these things, both with God and other people, is the beginning of a process of helping ourselves.

Binding up the broken-hearted

I remember once being asked to pray for a woman who was suffering with depression, apathy, bad dreams and a whole range of seemingly unconnected problems. As I struggled to find the words to pray to help her, the Holy Spirit whispered to me, 'Her heart is sick. Her hopes have been deferred too often.'

I asked the lady to tell me more about her life and it transpired that the Spirit's revelation was pertinently true. Her husband had divorced her, very much against her wishes, since she still loved him and wanted him back. So she spent four years praying and fervently, perhaps foolishly, believing that God would eventually bring him back to her and restore their marriage. Many of her friends encouraged her in her hopes, backed up, of course, with prophetic words and the like. She persevered in her dreams unswervingly, for month after month and year after year, ignoring the grim realities of her worsening situation as the divorce action followed its course through the courts.

It didn't happen. Her husband eventually married someone else. And the constant and repeated deferring of her hopes during those four years left the woman with a sick heart.

The broken or sick heart is a condition mentioned in the book of Proverbs, and it's one that afflicts many people – sadly, Christians as well as non-Christians. 'Hope deferred,' wrote King Solomon in Proverbs 13:12, 'makes the heart sick.'

The woman with the haemorrhaging in Luke 8:43–48 knew all about hope being deferred or delayed. Over a seemingly never-ending twelve-year period, she had been to doctors for help time after time. On each occasion she had parted with her money and somehow summoned up the desperate hope that perhaps they might be able to find a cure for her condition. But every time she ended up disappointed, and eventually she had become a penniless, cursed outcast in her community. Maybe some of us can appreciate the black, crushing feeling of pessimism that eventually engulfed her.

A sick heart is not a condition which should afflict a Christian. We should know how to avoid it. But sadly, we are sometimes more prone to it than non-Christians because the whole nature of our faith encourages us to hope for things we don't have. 'Now faith is being sure of what we hope for and certain of what we do not see,' we are told in Hebrews 11:1. But coping with the inevitable disappointments involved is not always easy. The heroes of faith like Abraham and Moses mentioned in the rest of that chapter had to learn to do so, and so must we. Abraham had hoped to father a multitude, but spent most of his life childless and then only managed to produce a few children, including Isaac. Moses never made it to the Promised Land (apart from standing with Jesus during the Transfiguration) because he became disobedient and set in his ways. And that was despite receiving a promise from God that he would one day possess it. But somehow they managed to continue walking with God until the day they died.

A sick or broken heart is something which is, in my experience, beyond human healing. Most conditions of the heart are. They need God's supernatural touch – the touch of the one who created and fashioned that heart in the first place. King David realised this when he cried out in Psalm 51:10, 'Create in me a pure heart, O God.' He knew that it was only the Almighty himself who could regenerate his wicked inner self and turn him into a new creation. We need to be mindful of this when attempting to counsel or pray for people with deep emotional hurts and wounds. There are some parts of a person's character which can, and should, be touched only by God himself. If we try to meddle in these areas ourselves we can cause even deeper wounds and stir up a host of other traumas. A lot of strange practices exist in some churches under the all-embracing banner of inner healing. And while there is no doubt in my mind that God does want to heal us of emotional hurts, we need to make sure that this healing is done the way Jesus did it, and not by using humanly inspired psychological meddling in people's pasts. The Holy Spirit is referred to in Scripture as the Finger of God, and we need to trust in his ability to put that finger on those tender, private areas of people's lives which are beyond human reach.

Having a sick heart is one of the most serious spiritual conditions that can afflict a Christian. Let's examine it.

The heart

Proverbs makes it clear that it is our *heart* that becomes sick. But what *is* our heart? The Hebrew word used to describe it is *leb*, which means something that is in the centre or in the middle of something. And although the Bible occasionally uses the word to refer to the human organ, it primarily uses it to describe our inner nature. It is the centre of our wisdom (1 Kings 3:12 and Prov 16:23) and our wills (Num 16:28, Judg 9:3 and 2 Chron 12:14).

Scripture attributes a whole range of human emotions and abilities to the heart. It is the place in the centre of our being where wisdom and understanding reside, along with our intuitive, or perceptive, natures (2 Kings 5:26). It is also the home of moral evil (Jer 17:9) and can be hardened (Ex 10:1, Josh 11:20). It can be fearful (Josh 5:1), glad (Ex 4:14), courageous (Ps 27:14) and display many other shades of emotion. It can be repentant (Ps 51:17), revived (Is 57:15) and can burn with zeal (Lk 24:32) – as Cleopas and his friend eventually found on the Emmaus road.

Our heart is the core of our being. It is the part of us that makes us who we are and governs our actions. And the Hebrew usage of the word 'heart' is also embraced in the English language, where we have phrases like 'my heart goes out to you', 'your heart's in the right place', 'a heart-to-heart talk', and 'from the bottom of my heart' to describe some of the deeper feelings within our humanity.

So when our heart becomes sick, the whole of our lives and our beings are affected . . . our wills, our minds, our emotions, and decision-making faculties . . . everything, in fact. No wonder that deferred hopes cause the most crippling damage. They blight the very core of who we are. And as far as I know, there is no other emotional condition mentioned in Scripture which strikes so seriously and so severely and with such devastating and long-lasting results.

It is impossible to under-estimate the power of our hearts. Ultimately, it's our hearts which determine what we do, or don't do, in life. If our heart is not in something, then we will eventually stop doing it. And if our heart desires something, we will eventually get it. To believe otherwise is to kid ourselves. King David surely had adultery in his heart long before he slept with Bathsheba. Judas no doubt had treachery in his heart long before he betrayed Jesus. Moses undoubtedly had murder and ambition in his heart long before he killed the Egyptian slave driver. With all these people, it only took the right circumstances for the real them – their hearts' desires, in other words – to come to the fore. Similarly, the person who quit your church in disillusionment had probably left in their heart long before they actually walked out of the door for the last time. And the woman who has been serving the Lord faithfully as a missionary in Africa for thirty years had probably already spent many years there in her heart before she left to go.

Jesus recognised the importance of the human heart when he told his disciples, 'For where your treasure is, there your heart will be also' (Mt 6:21). He understood the supreme strength of our hearts over our lives. That's why so much of his teaching was directed towards getting beneath our hypocrisy and veneer and touching our deepest heart attitudes. Jesus does not want an outward religious conformity from his disciples. He was scathing to the Pharisees and other religious leaders about this. No, he wants an inward reality – a clean, honest lifestyle that is the fruit of a clean, honest heart.

It is for these reasons that the book of Proverbs says more about the heart than any other book in the Bible, and warns us in 4:23: 'Above all else, guard your heart, for it is the wellspring of life.' That phrase 'above all else' indicates the immense significance given to this piece of advice. For if our hearts are wrong, then the very source of our life will become contaminated and every area of our lives – relationships, finances and ministry – will suffer as a result.

I remember once having a close relationship with a lovely couple whose hearts had been totally behind the church, its leaders and their vision for several years. But one night they had dinner with another couple who were seriously unhappy with all three. And it only took that one evening for the disgruntled couple to steal the hearts of the first couple. Almost overnight they became negative, critical and rebellious. The leaders, whom they had always trusted and respected, suddenly could do no right. Within weeks, all four had left the church, causing much unhappiness for themselves and others as they did so. The first couple had failed to guard their hearts. The result was conflict and pain for everybody involved. And I know of many other people who have left their churches, and even their partners, after having their hearts stolen by someone else. All of us can be prone to such attack, and if we don't guard our hearts properly, then we are sitting targets. Even hearts which are well guarded can still be vulnerable to seduction, disillusionment and discouragement. We should always be alert – and watching out for other people too.

Absalom, King David's son, was good at stealing people's hearts. We read in 2 Samuel 15:1ff how he waited by the city gate and intercepted people who were on their way to complain to the king. Then he would undermine the king's authority, subtly pointing out, 'If only I were appointed judge in the land! Then everyone who has a complaint or case could come to me and I would see that he receives justice.' Then in verse 6 we read, 'So he stole the hearts of the men of Israel.' It's easy to do. Always beware the person in your congregation who tells you they could do a better job than God's appointed leaders. They are probably an Absalom, and are trying to steal your heart.

When we become Christians God changes our hearts in a miraculous, supernatural way. As a result our hearts will want to praise God (Ps 9:1), cry out to him (Ps 84:2), seek him (Ps 119:2), sing and make music to him (Eph 5:19) and experience his love (Rom 5:5). But just because our hearts have been regenerated at conversion, that doesn't mean that they become immune to serious, often fatal wounds. It's naive to think otherwise, and to do so can result in our living in some strange kind of super-spiritual, pain-free stratosphere where we end up denying our humanity. For although our shields of faith should be strong enough to guard them from most wounds and attacks, we don't always use them, forgetting that our hearts are weak, vulnerable, and can change or get hurt very easily. That's why deferred hopes can deal a blow from which some people never recover.

The sickness

Proverbs talks about our hearts becoming sick. What does this mean? Is it a diagnosable condition like a cold or measles? What are the symptoms? It is important that we know, so we can recognise them in our own lives and in other people's too.

The Hebrew word that Solomon uses to describe this sickness is *chalah*, and it means 'sickness', 'weakness' or 'diseased'. It is used to describe three different types of condition.

First, there are physical illnesses, like the time when Joseph was told that his father Jacob was ill (Gen 48:1) or when the son of the widow of Zarephath became so sick that he died (1 Kings 17:17).

Then there are physical injuries, like those received by Ahaziah when he unfortunately fell through an upstairs window in 2 Kings 1:2, and those inflicted on King Joram by the Arameans in 2 Kings 8:29.

And lastly there are emotional conditions, like the sickness of heart we are looking at here. The word *chalah* is only used in connection with emotional weaknesses or sicknesses on two other occasions. They are both in the Song of Songs, where Solomon twice (Song 2:5 and 5:8) says he is sick, or more accurately faint, with love. How many of us remember that feeling during our early days of courtship! But in fact Solomon is the only writer in Scripture to use *chalah* in connection with emotional suffering. All the others use it only to describe physical sickness or injury. Maybe that's because this wise king had the revelation from God that our hearts can be hurt to such an extent that they literally become ill – even though such illnesses might never be diagnosed by a doctor. And the term 'faint' used in Song of Songs is certainly an apt one − I for one know that constantly deferred hopes can leave you feeble, defenceless and literally tottering through life with your head spinning. When your heart is sick, there is often a physical out-working of the condition. It may start with the emotions, but it normally results in our bodies being affected too.

The word *chalah* in the context of Proverbs 13:12 refers primarily to the *process* of becoming sick or weak, indicating perhaps that the condition is one which creeps up on us over a period of time.

After counselling hundreds of people with emotional problems over the years, I have no doubt at all that sickness of heart is a very real affliction, as real as cancer or arthritis or any other disease, and potentially just as deadly. And since it affects so many facets of someone's personality and character, it is sometimes very difficult to cure, especially when there are issues like resentment, anger and unforgiveness which clutter our hearts and block the healing which God wants to bring to us.

The cure

The broken heart is not usually something that mends with one simple prayer, although God can sometimes perform the most extraordinary miracles in an instant.

However, the good news is that binding up the broken-hearted was a central part of Jesus' mission (Lk 4:18–19).

He came from heaven to earth to deal with emotional problems, as part of his commission to preach the gospel and to heal those who were physically ill or afflicted with demons.

We can see this healing in action with the woman with heavy bleeding, mentioned earlier. For in the book of Mark we are told that Jesus healed her . . . and the word for healing there is the Greek word *sozo*, which has a far wider meaning than just physical healing. It means 'saved'. It's the word used throughout the New Testament to describe salvation. The King James Version more accurately renders this word as 'made whole'. In other words, Jesus did not just heal her physical condition, but saved her, which would have included bringing emotional and spiritual wholeness to her heart and life as well. Not only that, but he sent her away with peace of mind too (Mk 5:34), promising that her suffering was over. All this was achieved in the short time it took her to touch the hem of Jesus' garment and engage in a brief conversation with him. If we genuinely make contact with Jesus, then our hearts, bodies and lives can be changed in an instant, leaving us free to choose how we live our lives from then on. Either that or we begin a process of recovery which is slower but nonetheless equally effective.

Jesus still promises wholeness to anyone who is daring and desperate enough to reach out to him, as this demoralised woman did, in what must have been a last resort. It is impossible to say how he will heal our hearts, but we can be confident that he will – and he will probably use other people to do it. They may pray for us, they may listen to us, they may spend time with us and have meals with us. God will be there, right through. And eventually we will realise that we have changed inside, that we feel differently and that the surgery is complete.

6

Helping Others

My dentist reached for her drill. 'I can soon repair the damage,' she reassured me. I grunted, unconvinced. The problem was that *she* had caused a gaping hole in one of my teeth by prodding it too hard with one of her instruments. So her promises of help had a rather hollow ring to them. Similarly, there is little point in trying to help people who have become broken-hearted or disillusioned in church life if we were the cause of their problem! Before we start attending to their 'holes', we should take steps to avoid causing damage in the first place!

Churches are obvious places where disillusionment can occur. If you put people in close relationships for any length of time, then it is a cast-iron certainty that sooner or later they will begin to hurt one another and let one another down. It is inevitable, and the only solution is for each of us to learn tolerance and the ability to forgive, unendingly!

However there are two areas where many of us are prone to causing other people disappointment – and steps we can take to avoid doing so.

Prophetic madness

Our churches are often very prophetic these days and we love to build one another up with words from God about exciting futures and good times ahead. One girl of sixteen once asked me how she was going to find time to study for her 'A' levels when she had already received a number of prophecies indicating that she was going to lead churches, sing across the nation and travel the world for God! I've lost count of the number of young people I have met who have had words like this, plus guarantees of leadership prophesied over their lives. This is great – but who will be around to pick up the pieces of those who do not make it, for whatever reason? And more importantly, what about the people in the church whose ministry is to give out the hymn books and count the collection each week – the folk who are the real pillars of any strong, stable and mature local congregation? You don't often hear prophecies about people with this type of ministry.

Many prophecies nowadays tend to promise people more money, more power, bigger ministries, better homes and astonishingly successful futures; which may sound nice – after all, who wouldn't want these things? If we can't get them from the National Lottery, then perhaps the finger of God will point to us from heaven one day and say, 'Yes, it's you!'

However, you don't find many people in Scripture who

enjoyed lives like this or who got everything they had been promised. The ones who did, like King Solomon, usually ended up in a mess: his wealth, wisdom and power led him into sin!

I still long for the day when people prophesy scriptural truths like, 'You will give away your possessions to the poor' (NB to the poor, *not* to the church!) or 'You will be persecuted and people will say all kinds of evil against you' or even, 'You're finished, pal,' which was effectively what Agabus, the Judean prophet, told Paul in Acts 21:11. I wonder how such 'words' would be received by someone who was expecting to be told they will preach to the nations, lead churches and raise the dead?

Another problem is that modern prophecy tends to miss out the *conditional* element which is so important. All promises from God are dependent on us playing our part and obeying God in an ongoing way. Deuteronomy 28 clearly spells out the blessings which a child of God can expect from him but they are conditional on our obedience. The chapter starts with those crucial words, 'If you fully obey the Lord . . ..' And conversely, the curses for disobedience listed in the same chapter begin with 'If you do *not* obey the Lord your God . . ..' Most prophetic words should always be prefixed by those words 'If you . . .'. To miss them out is to put too little emphasis on people's daily responsibility to walk obediently with God if they are to enjoy his best.

Now, Scripture is clear in 1 Corinthians 14:3 that we should give words of prophecy to strengthen, encourage and comfort one another. Prophetic input is essential to our spiritual survival. But we need to weigh these words carefully. Sometimes they are just well-meaning waffle.

They don't build people up – they hype them up unrealistically. And the result is disillusionment on far too many occasions. I have heard people told they will be great leaders when it is clear they will never be any such thing, or that they will have major power ministries when it is obvious that they simply don't have a gifting in this area. A big crash is inevitable, either days, months or years later, when disappointment finally starts to bite, as it certainly will. Or maybe the person will feel so unable to fulfil the great 'word' upon their lives that they become guilty and condemned, and end up less effective for God than they were in the first place.

It is so easy to prophesy that a single person will find a partner when this is what they desperately want, that a sick husband will be healed when his partner is frantic to see him better, or that a childless woman will bear a child when this is what she has cried out for repeatedly over a long period of time. But are prophecies like these *really* what God is saying in these situations – or simply what we would *like* him to say? There is a vital and dangerous difference between the two; and giving people wrong words on sensitive issues like these literally risks their salvation itself. The disappointment involved in the word not coming true could end their walk with God for good. I know people who are living proof of the fact. God is not bound to keep our promises, even if they are made in his name. The name of Jesus is not a rubber stamp.

We need to be completely sure that we have heard God accurately and should then weigh the word with the person's friends, family or pastor before passing it on. Even if it is right, it might be best left unsaid. Each word of prophecy, knowledge or discernment should always be accompanied by a word of wisdom, probably from some-one else, to ensure it is applied correctly.

One girl I know was told by a prophet who was old and experienced enough to know better, 'You will marry an Austrian.' She had never thought of doing any such thing, and you can imagine the doubt and confusion that entered her life whenever she felt drawn to someone who wasn't Austrian. 'Words like this should always confirm what God has told you already,' I told her later. Fortunately, she had the common sense to work this out for herself and put the word well and truly on the back boiler – the best place for any kind of directional words which do not confirm what God has already said to us personally.

Our churches need to teach their people the whole truth about prophecy – that it may well be true and that they should weigh it and then pray it into being, diligently and faithfully. They should also be warned that the word could be wrong, or certainly questionable enough to place in the 'wait and see' category. It may take many years, or decades even, to come to pass, or it may not be answered in their lifetime. And it certainly will not come to pass at all if they do not play their part in its fulfilment. To fail to appreciate all these factors is to guarantee disillusionment further up the road. This is why every directional pro-phecy should be treated with the utmost caution and weighed up sensibly. It's naive to tell someone that an inaccurate prophecy was the result of a cheese supper rather than a prompting by the Holy Spirit when they've invested their hopes, their prayers and perhaps even their livelihoods and homes into seeing it fulfilled.

I remember once I was going through a difficult time because my two young boys had not slept well for weeks.

I was totally exhausted and so I asked a friend to pray with me. He began to prophesy that I would one day speak to crowds of thousands and perform miracles in Jesus' name. I didn't have the heart to tell him that all I wanted at that time was a hug of reassurance and a decent night's sleep! Prophecy in situations like this is often the last thing people want to hear – but is sometimes a lot quicker and more convenient than a listening ear and a cuppa which take time and commitment.

We also need to watch our own hearts when we give prophecies and to ask God for wisdom about the intentions of people who give them to us, especially if we don't know them. I know one chap who had decided to leave his church because he was profoundly unhappy with it. Word got back to the leaders and, lo and behold, he was called to the front of the following week's meeting and given a major 'word' about going out of God's will and how God would bless him if he stayed put. This, to my mind, was pure manipulation. Another man I know uses prophecies as a brilliant chat-up line with teenage girls. After all, what better opportunity to grab a pretty girl's attention than to seduce her with the word of the Lord? We need to be watchful.

Hasty promises

We Christians are terrible liars. No? Well, perhaps you're not like me! For I have lost count of the times I have promised people I'd pray for them and have forgotten all about it, or told them I'd get them round for dinner when I never really intended to. We used to have a saying in a house group I went to that if someone said, 'We really *must* get together sometime,' that meant you probably never would!

Perhaps you too make well-meaning but rash promises to people. In reality, they are little more than lies. And while we may forget about them as soon as the words leave our lips, the subsequent disappointment can leave people desperately discouraged when we don't do as we've promised. We need to take heed of the Scriptures: 'When a man makes a vow to the Lord or takes an oath to bind himself by a pledge, he must not break his word but must do everything he said' (Num 30:2). One day we will all have to give an account to God for every careless word we have spoken (Mt 12:36).

Sadly, church leaders are sometimes particularly susceptible to making hasty promises, usually without even realising it. Why? Because they have big hearts for people and would give them the world if they could. They want to motivate people and see them blessed and released into all that God has for them. As a result, they can let their words run away with them and speak before they think. You know the kind of thing: 'Next time I go out speaking, I'll take you with me' or 'I'll make sure we get you in the music group by the end of next month' or 'There's a really big future for you in this church.' I'm sure you could add dozens of other examples to the list! But they sometimes forget what they've said and even the fact that they've said it because they are so busy, speak to scores of people every week, and can't possibly keep track of every conversation they have had.

On the other hand, church members should always remember that their leaders are not God, Superman or the Pope. They will forget things and get it wrong sometimes. That is why it is so important that we invest our trust in Jesus, since he is the only one who will not let us down.

Now I have no doubt that those of us who make rash promises do so with the best of intentions. But we should always remember to choose our words wisely, because people, perhaps wrongly, often hang on to every word we say, and get terribly discouraged when the promise is not kept. A friend of mine advised me to always 'under-promise and over-deliver': in other words, to be sparing with what I promise people but generous in what I actually do for them; to do more than I say I will. That way, people end up pleased rather than discouraged. To do it the other way round, and to deliver less than you promise, is a quick route to causing people disillusionment.

The healing process

We have already seen how God intervenes and binds up broken hearts supernaturally in the previous chapter. But there is more to it than that. Nobody is capable of recovering from disillusionment on their own. They will need other people's help. And we all need to be prepared to reach out with support and love when it is needed. It may not be easy, for disillusioned people are hard to befriend and difficult to speak to. Even God himself was not able to get alongside Jonah after revival hit Nineveh, and an angel did not do much better with Elijah. Progress with the discouraged can be slow, because their defences are up and their wills are weak and lethargic.

There are some important stages involved in the healing process. We can see Jesus use some of them with the two disillusioned men on the road to Emmaus.

Drawing alongside people

Jesus drew alongside those two disciples gently – so gently, in fact, that they didn't even notice he was there to begin with. He entered their lives unasked, and simply walked with them, sharing their tedious journey and listening to their conversation. Initially, he didn't say much. He was simply there, not to criticise, not to counsel, not to rebuke, but to listen.

There comes a time, I believe, when God unfailingly draws gently alongside anybody who is suffering from deep disillusionment. You can count on it. And as with Cleopas and his friend, he will often do so unasked and so unobtrusively you don't even realise he is there. It's a sovereign act of his grace, and I have never known him to fail to provide it when it is really needed. David describes in the Psalms numerous occasions when God drew alongside him amid very dark times. In Psalm 6:3 he cries, 'My soul is in anguish. How long, O Lord, how long?' but goes on a few verses later to describe how God heard his weeping and his cry for mercy. And in Psalm 18 he relates how God rescued him and supported him when he was on the brink of death at the hand of Saul and his enemies.

Similarly, every time I have been through difficult times of disillusionment and pain, God has always broken in to my world in a tangible way. Of course, he was there already, because he never goes back on his promise not to leave us or forsake us. He assures us that he and his

Father will come and make their home with any believer
(Jn 14:23), and that tenancy agreement is one which lasts
for eternity. But it also seems that there is a time, when
we are hopelessly low and discouraged, that he eventually demonstrates his presence in a more tangible way.

You only have to read Genesis, the first book of the
Bible, to see God's commitment to draw alongside the
disillusioned. It seems that, right at the beginning of time,
he wanted to reveal himself as someone who seeks out
the suffering – even if they brought the suffering on
themselves. He did it with Adam and Eve in the Garden
of Eden. And the pages of Scripture from Genesis
onwards abound with similar tales. And what he did
then, he still does now, sometimes in the most unlikely
and surprising ways.

Sometimes, however, he will ask us to draw alongside
disillusioned people with him, or on his behalf. And we
can learn from Jesus' approach. We should be gentle, and
should not have any great agenda in mind other than to
love the person and be with them. We need to be
prepared to spend time with them, listening to their
complaints, hearing their hearts and just generally being
there for them. It could be a long time before they open
up to us, and maybe they never will. If they don't we
should not regard this as a failure, since a real hand of
friendship will be offered unconditionally, with no strings
attached. We need to spend time building trust and
should not be too quick to jump in with counsel, a
word of the Lord or some dazzling revelation about their
situation. The longer we spend on drawing alongside
people, the more fruitful our ministry will be, since we
will have earned the right to be heard.

Each of us has a duty to be sensitive to God's command to help a disillusioned person. It's not an easy call to obey. But the results could make the effort worthwhile.

Asking the right questions

After Jesus had drawn alongside Cleopas and his friend on the Emmaus road, he reached out to them by simply asking them a question. Even though he knew only too well why the two men were despondent, he still took the trouble to ask, 'What are you discussing together as you walk along?'

God is very good at asking questions. We should learn from him, and do the same. They may seem innocuous at first, but they are always the right ones to break a situation open. You can see him doing it right from the beginning of time. On that dreadful day when God discovered Adam and Eve hiding in the Garden of Eden, the words, 'Where are you?' were enough to cause the truth to come tumbling out (Gen 3:9ff). Of course, God knew exactly where Adam and Eve were before he asked. He knows everything. But the issue was that Adam and Eve had felt it necessary to hide at all. And because God did not normally have to go and hunt for his people to chat to them in the cool of the evening, those words 'Where are you?' spoke volumes about the awful situation which was unfolding.

God used exactly the same technique when he confronted Cain a while later, after he had committed the first murder in human history. 'Where is your brother Abel?' he asked in Genesis 4:9. Again, God knew full well what had happened to Abel. He reveals as much later in their conversation. But his question gave Cain the

chance to come clean – a chance which he rejected,
choosing to lie and reap the dreadful consequences
instead.

You find Jesus using seemingly innocuous questions just
as skilfully in the New Testament. The words 'Will you
give me a drink?' addressed to a highly immoral Samaritan
woman led to a conversation which did not just change her
life but also brought revival to her town (Jn 4:39).

And when Jesus asked his disciples, 'Friends, haven't
you any fish?' (Jn 21:5), his concern was not so much to
do with their skills or successes as fishermen, as to his
yearning to be with them again and, more importantly,
his desire to heal Peter from the disillusionment which
was crippling his life.

Someone once asked me why God needs to ask questions like these, since the answers are always apparent to
him already. My feeling is that asking questions and
listening to the answers are all part of building relationship. When I meet my seven-year-old boy from school, I
always ask him, 'What did you do today?'; and before he
opens his mouth, I know full well that he will probably
tell me that he did reading, writing, sums and played
football at break. But that's not the point. Far more
important is the fact that I love talking to my son and
want him to know that I care enough to ask him about his
day. If we did not bother to speak to God just because he
knows what we need before we ask him (and he *does* –
Mt 6:8), we will end up never speaking to him at all and
depriving ourselves of a friendship with him of any
depth or value.

It is important that when we spend time with a disillusioned person, we ask them questions. And if we ask

for God's help, he will enable us to be very wise in how we phrase them. The answers that come forth and the friendship that is established can ease the pain of disillusionment in often remarkable and unexpected ways. The conversation may begin with us asking an innocent question like, 'What have you been doing today?' – but may end up almost anywhere, with almost anything achieved along the way!

So we need to ask the right questions – ones which cannot be answered with a 'Yes' or a 'No'. And we need to be patient in listening to the answer, and not rush in, as many journalists do, with an interruption.

Confronting the truth

There has to come a time, as on the Emmaus road, when we have to face people with the truth about their situations. Sometimes we may have to listen to someone for a long time before we can deal with the real issues which caused their downfall. And sadly, in some cases, people may never allow us to get to this point at all. We may need to be patient and wait for the right time to present the truth and sometimes we will have to try time and time again, and use all kinds of different methods before we succeed.

It's a risky business, both for the disillusioned person, and the one trying to help, because there is a real possibility of both getting hurt. But as Proverbs says, the wounds from a friend can be trusted. Hopefully we will have such a good relationship with the disillusioned person that we will be able to take the risk of wounding them with the truth in order to bring greater good in the long run.

Yes, the truth can be painful. As the Christian author Jamie Buckingham once said, 'The truth will set you free, but first it will make you miserable.' Truth is rarely nice to hear.

Jesus certainly didn't mince his words on the Emmaus road. After listening to the two disciples, his response was very forthright: 'How foolish you are!' The King James Version is far more direct: 'O fools!' he said. And the word used there is *anoetos*, which refers not just to someone without any sense or someone who is lacking intelligence, but someone who should know better!

Jesus then went on to explain where the two men had got it wrong. He confronted their false hope – that Jesus was the one who was going to redeem Israel there and then – and dropped a plumbline of scriptural truth against it. He also confronted their ignorance and mis-understanding of God's promises, and set the record straight there too. In Luke 24:27 we are told that Jesus *explained* the Scriptures; and the Greek word for explain means 'to translate, expound, interpret'. In other words, he did a thorough job!

If we try to bring the truth to a disillusioned person we will need to be equally forthright and equally thorough. It is a bit like walking through a minefield. We may need to take time to listen tenderly and ignore some of the explosions that occur along the way. Our job is to burst the bubbles, to demolish the castles in the air and bring the person to the point where they can see where they have invested in false hopes. It can be a painfully sad process, but it is a necessary one if the person is ever to have any kind of realistic faith again and to reach the point where they make a complete recovery from the past.

Yes, the truth will set people free – if they can cope with it. The problem is that not many people can. In fact God's people have a particularly bad track record when it comes to receiving home truths. Virtually every Old Testament prophet who tried to tell it like it was, met an early death. Jesus laid it all out in black and white to the Scribes, Pharisees and religious leaders of his day and got killed for it too. So did Stephen. Even Jesus had to back-pedal once while explaining the truth to his disciples. 'I have much more to say to you, more than you can now bear,' he told them (Jn 16:12). He knew that the twelve would not be able to cope with hearing much more, with his arrest and execution imminent.

Whenever I hear that a recognised preacher has been banished from a particular church after speaking there, I always think to myself, 'I bet he told them the truth.' Usually, the purer the truth, the greater the reaction. Try going to *your* church leader and telling him the truth about your church and see the reaction! Or better still, get him to come to *you* and set out the truth about your life! If you don't actually kill him there and then, the chances are you will go away plotting it in your heart for a while. We all do. That's why God often has to bring us to a very low point in our lives before we are prepared to listen to anything other than the things we want to hear.

Nowadays we may not physically kill people for telling the truth, but we still have our ways of silencing anybody who rocks the boat and disturbs the *status quo*, whether it's within our circle of friends, our church or our denomination or stream. We isolate them, sideline them, don't ask them back to speak, or we subtly assassinate their characters with sly references to 'issues' in their lives. Anything, in fact, to shut them up.

Truth is sobering. But the disillusioned person must hear it, spoken lovingly, probably by a friend. And if God asks us to be that friend, we must repeatedly stress that we understand why the person feels the way that they do but that the truth is something different. It's painful. But I have found that when people learn to live with the reality of their God, their church, themselves and the nitty-gritty issues of life, they quickly become happier and more stable.

It's important to see that Jesus based his truth on Scripture. This is essential, because the Bible provides us with an objective plumbline. When we're talking to a disillusioned person, it's easy to end up arguing with them about their situation and wrestling our opinion against theirs. This achieves little. But as we start to mention what the Scriptures say about life issues, then we can have the confidence that the Holy Spirit will make our words living and active in the mind and heart of the hearer.

I'm not suggesting that we sit over a cup of tea and read a disillusioned person the first ten chapters of Leviticus! Jesus did not hit Cleopas and his friend with Scripture. Rather, he applied the word to their lives, a bit like applying ointment to a wound. So to say to a disillusioned person that maybe it was a bit unrealistic of them to expect to be working full time for the church just eighteen months after joining it when Paul waited seventeen years before God used him . . . well, it sets people's feelings in a proper biblical context, doesn't it?

Yes, confronting the truth is an essential part of the

healing for a disillusioned person. It will make them or break them. But it's better to risk confronting it and failing than nodding in agreement and leaving the person just as fed up and full of unreality as they were in the first place.

Once this critical stage has been dealt with – and it might take God and whoever he chooses to use a long time – then hopefully we can move on to the next part of the renewal programme!

A reassuring word

Sometimes people don't need deep ministry. They just need some assurance that they are doing all right and that everything is okay between them and God. Satan is the master of condemnation and manages to make Christians feel guilty over just about everything without them even realising it. If we are honest, most of us don't think we are doing particularly well with our Christian lives. We feel we don't pray enough, are hopeless with evangelism, don't often read God's word, should be more committed to the church, hardly ever fast . . . and maybe some of these things are true.

However we need to take time to see things the way God sees them. In Matthew 25, Jesus told his disciples the parable of the sheep and the goats.

> Then the righteous will answer him, 'Lord, when did we see you hungry and feed you, or thirsty and give you something to drink? When did we see you a stranger and invite you in, or needing clothes and clothe you? When did we see you sick or in prison and go to visit you?' (Mt 25:37–38)

The implication here appears to be that these righteous people were unaware of some of the good they had done.

But they were given the assurance that their king had seen it and had noted it.

We have the same assurance, and need to reassure others that God noticed, and remembers all those times when they invited someone in for a cup of coffee, when they took some flowers to a neighbour, when they picked up a friend's child from school or helped a stranger push their car.

7

Moving Forward

It is New Year's Eve and the revelries are in full swing. Everybody is in the party mood, full of fun, merriment and laughter. Inevitably, someone eventually starts playing the hokey-cokey on the piano and within seconds everyone has joined hands in a raucous circle, swinging into the middle and then hurtling out again to the words 'In-out-in-out, shake it all about.'

Church life and the Christian walk can be a bit like that. One minute you're 'in' – right in the centre of everything that is going on. You are making friends, are popular, are heavily involved in various activities, and generally 'going on with God'. But then maybe you cross swords with your leaders, or are misunderstood in a situation. Maybe someone has gossiped about you or spread rumours. Maybe you have made a mistake and feel ashamed of facing people. Maybe you have fallen out with someone. Or maybe you have some difficult issues to face at home, at work or in your character. In circumstances like these, it does not take much for rejection, fear and isolation to set in, and move you from the centre to the fringes of church life. Getting back to the middle can, for some of us, be very difficult and take a long time.

Take your seats . . .

Our churches' seating plans say a great deal, if you know how to interpret them. They are very often the same, no matter which church you go to. The front two rows normally comprise the people who are 'in', right up to their necks. They are first to arrive, last to leave, first to stand to sing, quick to pray and are generally happily involved in everything that is going on. Also in the front row are the leaders, who always tend to sit together – safety in numbers, perhaps! – along with those who think they *should* be leaders and those who are desperately trying to become one.

However, the story changes as you start to move back beyond the first two rows. As you go further back, you discover more and more people who are on the fringes of church life. And when you get to the back row, you often find the people who are very much 'out'. The back row of any church, whether it contains pews, seats or beanbags, always tells its own stories, and many of them are heartbreaking. It is normally occupied by people who are hurt, disillusioned and misunderstood, who think, rightly or wrongly, that they don't fit or think they aren't welcome and who have therefore retreated to the fringes; either that or they have put themselves there through sin, lack of repentance or lack of faithfulness. Or maybe they have an over-inflated opinion of themselves, and sit at the back and sulk because their 'leadership qualities' have not yet been recognised. Yes, they are 'in' church and yes, they are 'in' the meeting. But in reality they are neither. Their bodies might be there, but their hearts are miles away.

Comforting the afflicted . . .

Pastors should always be looking out for church members who are on the fringes, or who have retreated there. For although at first glance they might seem hard, unapproachable and unenthusiastic, very often all these symptoms are just a cry for help and in reality they are desperate for attention. We should never take folk like this at face value. Their 'Keep away' sign is often just a frightened façade.

The fringes of church life are a lonely, dangerous place to be. Peter describes the devil as someone who 'prowls around like a roaring lion, looking for someone to devour' (1 Pet 5:8). This analogy is an apt one. When a lion is getting ready to attack, it spends a long time watching a herd, waiting for one of the animals to stray from the others. When this happens, it will pounce. Strays in church life are equally vulnerable – to sin, deception, bad attitudes, forming cliques and damaging the church. There is safety within the body of the church and if we aren't there, we need to do everything we can to get there. And each of us has a responsibility to try and draw alongside the back-row brigade and try and draw them in. We need to pray for them and win them with love. For people's hearts are fickle and gullible. Disappointments, bad company and the general humdrum of church life can, within minutes, contaminate a heart which took years to win. The primary aim of our relationships, whether in marriage or in church life, should always be to win people's hearts and keep on winning them. Unless we do so, we will never have friendships of any depth or lasting value. That is why Jesus talks about winning our brothers over when we attempt to solve relationship disputes (Mt 18:15). It is sometimes easy to win an argument, but we can lose a friend's heart in the process.

Getting beneath the surface

Pastors need to take great care when dealing with the back-row groups of people who are disillusioned. It is easy either to ignore them completely, or to over-react to their looks, their sin and their attitudes. Often they have colonised, as I mentioned earlier, and it is tempting to rush in and start accusing them of being a clique, or causing disunity and of gossiping. Such actions might well be justified and it is quite likely that these things are true. But rash confrontations usually do more harm than good and may force people out of the church and away from God for good. Remember, pastors will one day have to give an account for these people's souls!

It is better to gently try to win one person at a time through love and tender listening. In doing so, we must avoid being dragged down ourselves. This is why Paul warns in Galatians 6:1, 'Brothers, if someone is caught in a sin, you who are spiritual should restore him gently. But watch yourself, or you also may be tempted.' I have found time after time that when you listen to a disillusioned person, you will find that their perceptions and opinions are valid but very distorted and completely unhelpful. And unless we are strong we can end up getting entangled in their attitudes and opinions rather than helping to solve them. It takes a special kind of strength to be able to listen tenderly to someone's moans and groans, not get drawn into them, and yet at the same time avoid giving the person the idea we're rejecting them simply because we disagree with them.

Normally, behind every grumble and bad attitude is a wound that needs healing. And we need to try and focus on that, no matter how ghastly and unappealing the symptoms are. Jesus was able to do that. He reached out and expressed love to the woman caught in adultery in John 8:4, seeing beyond her sin and shame. He even drove a horse and cart through the law of Moses (Lev 20:10) which demanded that she be put to death for her actions, although in accepting her, he in no way accepted her actions. 'Go now and leave your life of sin,' he told her. We need to try and develop hearts like that – tender enough to break a few rules in order to love people and rescue them, but clear enough to discern, and explain the rights and wrongs of their situations. For while love may tenderly overlook a sin issue at first, it will not be true love if it does not address it at some point.

Of course, those in the back row have a clear responsibility to do something themselves to change their situation. At the end of the day we all have a personal duty to work out our salvation ourselves – not to sit and wait for our long-suffering pastors to carry us. There has to come a point in our lives where, no matter what we have been through, we make the choice to push through, especially in praise and worship. You always find that people who do this rarely stay on the fringes for long. God responds to their sacrifice in all kinds of ways. And there are no excuses for failing to do this. The Gadarene demoniac, afflicted as he was by thousands of demons, was still able to fall on his knees and worship Jesus, *before* he was delivered. His will was intact. And if he can do it, so can we!

Going our separate ways

Now it could be that restoration and healing ultimately prove to be impossible; people don't always want help or perhaps are not prepared to change. They are stuck in their attitudes and sometimes are quite happy to cause trouble. In this case, it is best that they leave the church, as quickly as possible – the sooner the better. In many situations I have found that if people become seriously hurt or disillusioned in a church, leaving is often the best option. Whether the issue was their fault or someone else's is irrelevant. Healing cannot always be given in the place and by the people who perhaps caused the hurt, for the wounded people are often unable to receive it there. This does not mean that we leave church every time we get hurt – far from it! Church-hopping is far too prevalent these days and we all need to develop the attitude that we are there for life. It's the only way we will ever build anything solid.

But there are extreme cases when moving on is the only way out of a situation. Hopefully, this can be done with friendship, dignity and love rather than amid angry recriminations and blood-letting. I once met a man who wanted to leave his church and was subjected to four hours of close questioning by his leadership before they would let him leave with their blessing. They needed to be sure he was leaving cleanly, they said – but the treatment smacked more of Orwellian *1984*-style thought-cleansing than anything I have ever seen in Scripture. For while we need to try and resolve issues before we move on, meetings like the one I have just described achieve little other than causing more hurt. Pastors and leaders need to give people the freedom to walk away with their blessing, owing them nothing, even if they think they are wrong or are glad to see the back of them!

There is nothing wrong with going our separate ways. Amos says, 'Do two walk together unless they have agreed to do so?' (3:3). There is no point in staying in a congregation where we don't agree with the vision, the ethos and the leadership. To remain causes stress not just to us but everybody else. And to remain, as if on some God-sent mission to try and change things is usually nothing other than spiritualised rebellion. Some people are not called to be certain pastors' sheep – and some pastors are not called to be certain sheep's shepherds. The earlier this is recognised, the better. Paul and Barnabas went their own ways in the most acrimonious circumstances, and there is no record of them ever working together again. Yet God blessed them in their respective ministries, with Paul finding the grace to praise Barnabas later (1 Cor 9:6). And similarly, Abram and Lot went their separate ways in Genesis 13:12. Separating need not be a problem.

Dare to discipline

In some cases involving groups of disillusioned or fringe people, discipline is the only way forward, although leaders should always beware bringing discipline too soon unless a situation has deteriorated to such an extent that other people are being hurt. For while putting difficult people out of the church may be the easiest course of action, it is not always the wisest. We should remember that Jesus never excluded Judas from anything, even though he knew he was a thief and had betrayal in his heart. Instead, he treated him like a close friend (Jn 13:26–28) by giving him a piece of bread at the Last Supper while at the same time giving him the freedom to make his own decisions.

I am sure many modern churches would have expelled Judas for his moral failings at a much earlier stage, along with James and John for being ambitious and power-hungry (Mt 20:20–21), Peter for committing grievous bodily harm (Jn 18:10) and Thomas for a serious doubt problem (Jn 20:25). Yet Jesus used them, warts and all. His approach was always gentle and patient and he never stripped them of their functions or excluded them from ministry because they failed or had character deficiencies.

I have often heard church leaders say, 'You cannot build a church on needy people.' But perhaps they forget that this is exactly what Jesus did! He got hold of a dozen men who had all manner of character deficiencies which might have disqualified them from holding any kind of office in some modern churches and used them to start one of the most successful churches in history. That doesn't mean to say that we start giving positions of leadership and responsibility to people with serious pastoral issues. There is a difference between people who have 'needs', like we all do, and people who are seriously 'needy' and not yet ready to function effectively in church life. But maybe we need to be more adventurous in our choices of leaders sometimes and be prepared to take as many risks as Jesus did.

When discipline is necessary and people are asked – or told – to leave the church, pastors should always try to follow my father's advice. 'Never slam a door. You never know when you might need to go back through it,' he would say when I got irate in different situations. We always need to give room for a person under discipline to come back, much as we might not want them to! The immoral brother in the Corinthian church (1 Cor 5:1–5) was prescribed some pretty heavy treatment by Paul, including putting him out of church and even handing him over to Satan. Paul had no choice in the situation – the man was clearly unrepentant. Yet in 2 Corinthians 2:5–8 Paul says, 'The punishment inflicted on him by the majority is sufficient for him. Now instead, you ought to forgive and comfort him, so that he will not be overwhelmed by excessive sorrow. I urge you, therefore, to reaffirm your love for him.' Assuming that he is writing about the same person, Paul was happy to allow the man back in and not keep any record of his wrong, apparently because he had come to a place of repentance. Pastors need to ask themselves the hard question: are they in a position to offer forgiveness, comfort and love to those people whom they have disciplined or expelled from the fellowship if they repent and want to return? Or was the discipline carried out with such severity so as to make this impossible?

Of course, discipline does not always mean expelling people from church. It can come in a variety of shapes and forms, depending on the situation. But ultimately, a pastor or leader cannot apply discipline to someone's life unless the person is willing to receive it. Some people, sadly, are not prepared to submit to discipline by God, or anybody else. The tragedy of their state is unfortunately usually obvious to everybody else but themselves.

Running away

Many disillusioned people try to solve their problems by running away, and, while it is a completely normal reaction, it achieves precisely nothing! Of course it's not always easy to physically get up and go these days – our mortgages, negative equity and credit card debts make sure of that. But you still find that people will sometimes change jobs, leave their church, move house, change partners or even divorce rather than face the disillusionment they are feeling.

It's an understandable reaction – after all, who wouldn't want to get away from the cause or the scene of the hurt just as quickly as possible? But it's not a very wise one, for you always find that when you run away, you take your pain with you. You might change your circumstances, but your heart will remain the same until God intervenes and heals it. Jonah is a good example of this. He had a serious attitude problem to God; his heart was wrong and it stayed that way, despite going the opposite direction to the one which God had commanded, being thrown in the sea, swallowed by a whale, seeing revival break out in Nineveh and having God come and counsel him personally about it all afterwards. How sad that the book about him ends suddenly, even prematurely perhaps, with his heart in the same rebellious state that it was at the beginning. He didn't change, despite God's dealings with him.

Several other Bible characters discovered that running away simply doesn't work. Adam and Eve did it for the first time in the Garden of Eden and soon discovered that God comes looking for you. And Elijah is another good example. After his awesome heaven-fire showdown with the prophets of Baal on Mount Carmel, he suffered from a classic case of burn-out and ran off alone into the desert near Judea, where he found a juniper tree and sat and sulked. Even the intervention of a friendly angel did not do much to cheer him up. So he went off on his own again, without bothering to ask God or to pray about what to do. This time he embarked on a forty-day trek to Mount Horeb, where he arrived still sulking. It took a personal intervention from God himself (1 Kings 19:15) to help him see that being alone was not doing him any good and that what he needed was to get back to work – to anoint Hazael king over Aram, Elisha as his own successor and to help Hazael and Jehu, the king of Israel, to defeat God's enemies. Elijah didn't need isolation. He needed company and he needed to keep busy. God's mercy to Elijah here was incredible. He made sure he had enough food and sleep for the journey to Mount Horeb, even though the trip was against his will. And he was patient with him when he initially disobeyed the instruction to stand on the mountain (1 Kings 19:11).

God still sticks with us, even when we are out of his will and disobedient.

King David, too, spent periods of his life hiding from God and from people. He eventually admitted in Psalm 139, 'Where can I go from your Spirit? Where can I flee from your presence? If I go up to the heavens, you are there; if I make my bed in the depths, you are there. If I rise on the wings of the dawn, if I settle on the far side of the sea, even there your hand will guide me' (vv. 7–10). He discovered that there is no point in hiding (Ps 11:1), because God himself is our hiding place (Ps 32:7), and when we run, God has already arrived at where we are going before we've left to get there!

Peter is another example. He suffered terrible pain and disillusionment after denying he knew Jesus just when Jesus needed him most. Who knows what he went through as he stood and watched his beloved Saviour and friend suffer at the hands of his enemies? And after shedding some very bitter tears, he coped with his pain, torment and the boring inactivity which came after Jesus' death by announcing to his friends, 'I'm going out to fish' (Jn 21:3). In other words he wanted to do what we all do when the going is tough: to turn the clock back and run away to the painless 'good old days' when he was a Galilean fisherman and nothing else. The days of being a member of Jesus' ministry team were over. After all, he had to earn a living to provide for his family! But of course, his decision didn't achieve anything, because the issue wasn't whether his future lay in being a fisherman or a church planter. It was more important than that. His heart needed healing and it took a miracle, a tasty barbecued breakfast and then a personal intervention by

Jesus to heal him and set him back on the road to effectiveness again (Jn 21:15–22). It is wonderful how Jesus
knew exactly where to find Peter and also knew his
physical needs as well as his emotional ones. He knew
that Peter had not caught any fish that night, so he
brought some of his own. That's just one example of
how much God cared about him. Indeed, Jesus was
watching out for Peter, right from the time of his resurrection. In Mark 16:7 the angel told the two Marys at the
empty tomb, 'But go, tell his disciples *and Peter*, "He is
going ahead of you into Galilee. There you will see him,
just as he told you."' That's how much Jesus loved Peter
and was concerned about him.

It seems that almost everybody in Scripture who tried
to run from their pain and their God found it achieved
nothing. For God's heart of love always pursues us in
order to get behind that 'Leave Me Alone' sign and bring
us to a place where he can heal and restore us. Men, I
think, are more prone to run away from their feelings
than women. Perhaps that's why the women stayed at the
foot of the cross until Jesus died while most of the men
were nowhere to be seen.

I remember trying, rather helplessly, to comfort a dear
friend after his wife suddenly died. 'I think I'll move
straight away,' he said. I encouraged him not to change
anything for at least a year, since he was too emotionally
torn to be able to make any sensible decisions about his
future at the time. Later on he was glad he stayed put.
Staying in those familiar surroundings gave him a secure
place where God could begin to deal with the awful pain
that was tearing his heart in two. Even though those
surroundings were full of hurt and memories, they

were still the appropriate place to grieve. I found the same when I was mourning the death of my father. I went here, there and everywhere to try and cope with the searing agony of bereavement. But wherever I went, the pain went too. Eventually I discovered that the only way to help myself was to stop running and let God deal with me amid the normal, everyday circumstances of life and in familiar surroundings.

Now, there *are* times when we need to be alone for a while to deal with our pains and our sorrows. There is nothing wrong with this. When Jesus heard the terrible news of his cousin John the Baptist's death at the hands of King Herod in Matthew 14:13, he withdrew, by boat, to be on his own. But he didn't flee – far from it. When 5,000 needy men, plus women and children, tracked him down and arrived for ministry and a bite to eat, he didn't shoo them away. Instead he was filled with compassion, set his own feelings aside for a while and healed them and fed them – hardly the petulant actions of someone who is saying, 'I want to be alone!' It was only after he had met the needs of the crowd that he dismissed them, packed his disciples off on a boat and went off on his own in the hills for a while, using the miracle of walking on the water to get back on schedule later on. There's a world of difference between withdrawing for a while and running away altogether.

It is significant that Cleopas and his friend headed for Emmaus at their time of disillusionment. Perhaps it was their home – we cannot be sure. But it was certainly a place famed for its spectacular views. You could literally see for miles in all directions: the lush hill country of Ephraim to the north, the wildernesses of Judea to the south, the twinkling blue Mediterranean to the west and Jericho and the Dead Sea to the east.

Maybe Cleopas and his friend felt that if they went to Emmaus they would be able to enjoy the views and forget about their real feelings, or perhaps be able to see their situation more clearly and from a different perspective.

But running away rarely changes things. It might ease the pain but it certainly will not cure it. Changing our physical circumstances rarely, if ever, cures disillusionment because what is needed is a change of heart, not a change of scenery. Once God has dealt with us on the inside, then perhaps a change in circumstances, like a new house, a new church or a new job (but not a new marriage partner!) may help. I have lost count of how many times God has refused to change my circumstances until he has changed my heart. Frustratingly, his priorities are different from ours, but he does know what is best for us in the long run.

Withdrawing

It is also possible to run away without going anywhere! In other words, rather than change our circumstances, we stay where we are, but retreat in our hearts. We let friendships drift, we give ourselves to no one, we build a wall round ourselves, we get to the meetings late, sit in the back row and leave early. We haven't actually left but we may as well have done, since the results are pretty much the same. We have run away and hidden in the gloomy safety of our hearts. It's not nice – but it seems to be nicer than any other option.

I had a really deep friendship with a chap once; it was

one of those relationships where we really touched hearts regularly over a number of years. Every time we met, we would pour out our latest news along with everything that was going on in our lives. We had no secrets and knew everything there was to know about one another. But then he went through a down time and eventually 'ran away' in his heart. Although he was always warm and friendly whenever we met, it was impossible to get to the real him any longer. He was distant and remote and no matter how much we chatted and prayed together, I just couldn't reach him. How sad.

It is so easy to do this in any kind of relationship – especially those, like marriage, which are particularly close in the first place. Some couples still live in the same house and share the same bed, but as far as real intimacy is concerned, they might as well be on opposite sides of the world! They have withdrawn from one another.

We know that Peter withdrew from Jesus after denying him just before the crucifixion. And although the two met several times after the resurrection, Jesus appears to have had difficulty reaching the *real* him. He had to ask him three times – presumably redeeming the three occasions when Peter had denied Jesus – whether he still loved him when they chatted after that breakfast on the sunny shores of Lake Galilee. But it wasn't until the third time that Jesus penetrated Peter's defences and exposed his true feelings. 'Peter was hurt because Jesus asked him the third time, "Do you love me?",' we are told in John 21:17. The issue was one of love, and the hurt had to come out. Once it had, Peter was once again able to obey when Jesus said, 'Follow me,' a few moments later. He followed – hesitantly, questioningly, but he went. His guard had come down, the relationship was restored and Peter continued to follow Jesus unflinchingly until the day he died.

Now, withdrawing can take two forms.

Withdrawing from people

Withdrawing from people means that we maintain a 'Me and God' relationship which nobody else is part of. We relate to him and that's as far as it goes. He is our counsellor, our teacher, our pastor, our everything. But relating to him and not to his body almost always results in spiritual deception of one kind or another. For while he is our Lord, he also puts men and women around us to lead us, pastor us, admonish us, teach us, and generally be our friends – or enemies! When Jesus commissioned the eleven apostles in Matthew 28:16–20, he told *them* to make disciples. It was a job *they* would do, not him. And so when you meet someone who claims they are being discipled by God, they probably aren't being discipled by anybody. There is no place for independence in the body of Christ. That's why Jesus commanded us to pray '*Our* Father' in Matthew 6, rather than *my* Father. We're in it together or not at all. For while I'm sure we could all live great Christian lives on a desert island with the Trinity for company, we would remain spiritual babies, for it is God's people, his human ministries, who bring us to maturity (Eph 4:11–13).

Withdrawing from God

On the other hand, withdrawing from God is just as dangerous. We end up relating to everybody else but him. We go to church, sing, join in the activities and even pray. But when it comes to that important day-to-day walk with him, where we meet with him to pray and allow him to speak to us from his word, well, nothing happens. The intimacy and love have disappeared. Other people might think that we are going on great with God because we are able to act the part in public. But only God sees what is – or isn't – happening in private.

So withdrawal, whether it's from God or from people, is a completely understandable reaction when we are hurt and disillusioned. But it tends to lead nowhere. If we genuinely want our broken hearts to be healed, we must strive to avoid making things worse for ourselves, and do what we can to co-operate with God's healing and restoration programme.

Encouraging reality

So much heartbreak could be avoided in church life if we encouraged reality at every level. Sadly, churches are sometimes the hardest place to be 'real'. You could even say that our faith militates against it! I have lost count of the number of occasions when people have told me the barmiest, stupidest things after church meetings, yet because they are 'brothers and sisters in the Lord', there is a pressure to agree with them and bless them when deep down all you want to do is send for the men in white coats.

I remember once nodding earnestly as a brother confided in me how Satan himself had slammed his car bonnet lid on his head while he was changing his oil. Later, I thought to myself, 'Where else on earth apart from church could someone come out with such claptrap and not be told they were mad!'

The problem is that because God does sometimes work in peculiar ways, we feel a pressure to expect him to operate weirdly all the time. And we tend to think that because God uses the foolish to confound the wise, the stupider they are, the wiser they must be! Sometimes we are more spiritual than God is and deny him the chance to work extraordinarily through the everyday circumstances of life. In our supernatural relationships with God, we should always remember that it is he who is super, and we who are natural – not the other way round!

There are a few steps we can take to discourage weirdness and unreality in church life and thereby do everybody a favour in saving them some heartbreak further up the road.

1. *Faith does* NOT *deny the facts*

We have all met the people in church who are confessing their legs are better while walking on crutches. Some such instances are dishonouring to God. When Jesus healed someone, they were healed! There were no periods of time when they went around confessing they were healed when they plainly were not. Quite the reverse: Jesus actively encouraged them to get their healing tested out by their family or the priest so there could be no doubt about it.

There is nothing wrong with holding on to God's promises faithfully and waiting for them to come to pass. But there is all the difference in the world between doing that and lying by saying we are healed when we are not, or saying we possess something when we don't. Faith does not deny the facts – it rules them. If we are holding out for healing for backache, but are still in a lot of pain, then the truth is that we are in pain. But the *greater* truth is that Jesus took that sickness on the cross and we are waiting and believing for that to be worked out in our life.

2. *Look at others' track records*

A man once came up to me and said God had told him to pray for £350,000 to buy a new house. I was sceptical but not because God doesn't sometimes give people huge sums of money to buy expensive homes. I am sure he does! No, my doubts were based on the fact that the chap's record in terms of faith didn't justify his claim. It seemed to me that praying in such a huge sum was way beyond him. As things turned out, the man didn't get the money or the house, and was bitterly disappointed about it. Maybe someone should have been honest enough to say to him, 'Such a sum isn't in your league, mate!' Similarly, whenever people tell you that God is going to use them to raise the dead, ask them to demonstrate the effectiveness of their healing ministry next time you have a sore throat! Then you will see where their faith is really at! We all need to have a realistic assessment of our faith and to operate within these limits.

3. *Avoid chasing blessings*

A brother once told me he had flown 8,000 miles to visit a church in order to get a word from the Lord.

'Did God speak to you?' I asked him.

'He certainly did,' the man replied. 'A man came up to me right out of the blue and told me to love my wife.' I scratched my head and wondered why he had to travel all that way, at enormous cost, to hear something which was written quite plainly in his Bible!

There is a strong tendency in churches nowadays to go chasing round the world to catch up with the latest blessing. Although there is no doubt that some people have had some significant encounters with God by visiting churches where God's Spirit is moving powerfully, 'blessing-hopping' can display a susceptibility that ignores Jesus' warnings in Matthew 24:26: 'So if anyone tells you, "There he is, out in the desert," do not go out; or, "Here he is, in the inner rooms," do not believe it.' At the end of the day, God will move anywhere he finds faith and hunger. And revivals cannot be copied. Just because God is moving in a particular way in one place does not mean that he will do the same in our church, even if we try to use the same 'formula' to achieve a blessing. The key to revival in any church is for the congregation to seek God and to cry out for him to move in a way that is ideal for each local situation – not one thousands of miles away that is different in culture, geography and church history.

Pastors have a great responsibility here to avoid raising their congregation's hopes that each new wave of blessing is *the* answer. It probably isn't – and the church will end up going up and down like a yo-yo. If there is one thing that is *the* answer, it is the promise that Jesus gave his disciples: 'I will build my church. . . .' Sometimes I am convinced he would be able to do so more effectively if we were less busy trying the latest method or formula!

4. We're in a marathon, not a sprint

So many people start their Christian lives well but finish them badly, or, even worse, don't finish them at all. And sometimes our teaching in church is to blame. For, in an attempt to keep people's interest, we tend to keep them fired up like sprinters all the time and then wonder why they burn out. We need to prepare people for a marathon that lasts a lifetime and not be afraid to let people know that it is not a failing if life is occasionally boring and dull. Paul wrote to Timothy, 'I have finished the race, I have kept the faith' (2 Tim 4:7). That was after years and years of faithfully serving God in the most trying circumstances. Hopefully we will be able to say the same one day, and when things are tough, consider ourselves lucky that we don't have a lifespan of 650 years as Enoch did!

8

Building for the Future

You could cut the atmosphere with a knife. The man I
was counselling was angry and deeply disillusioned.
Tears flowed down his cheeks as he shouted at me,
'You don't understand. I've been left without hope.' As
the story unfolded, it emerged that his church leaders
had brought discipline to his life in such a way that he
had nothing to look forward to, nothing to aspire to any
longer. And although the discipline had certainly been
necessary, it lacked one vital ingredient – the element of
redemption. That's why it had left this particular chap in
such a state. For God's discipline always has the ingredient of future hope within it. So should ours. For people
cannot live without hope.

The Tyndale New Bible Dictionary puts it very well:
'Hope is a psychological necessity if man is to envisage
the future at all.' In other words, without hope we are
lost. For God has created men and women to be people
who have a natural tendency to carry on hoping, even
when there are no real grounds for doing so.

Everyone you meet is hoping for something: a new job, more money, a better car, a long holiday, a Happy New Year . . . the list is endless. This is natural. But if we're honest, some of the things we hope for are unrealistic. They are dreams. And any West Ham fan will tell you what happens to dreams. Like pretty bubbles in the air, they fade and die. It's sad. But very often it's true.

Politicians, the media and the advertising industry tend to encourage us to hope for things that will never happen. Their whole ethos is that the best is yet to come. But they don't tell you how to cope with the disappointment when those generally unrealistic dreams are not fulfilled. And the reality is that they generally aren't. The problem many of us face is that when we become Christians, we bring the same thought patterns into God's kingdom, grab hold of the concept that we should hope for the impossible, and set ourselves up for hurt and broken hearts. We fail to recognise that biblical hope is completely different. The Greek word for hope is *elpis*, which means 'to desire some good, with the expectation of obtaining it'. In other words, biblical hope is based on certainty. And unless we grasp this, we will suffer a lifetime of paralysing disappointments as Christians.

It's because biblical hope is based on certainty that the writer to the Hebrews is able to refer to it (6:19) as an 'anchor for the soul, firm and secure', and Paul is able confidently to assure the Romans (5:5) that it 'does *not* disappoint us'. If we base our hopes on certainties, then it is possible to have hope and not get disappointed in the process, as so many of us have done in the past.

Hoping for the right things

The Scriptures say that there are eight main things which we can reliably hope for. If we put our hope in them, then we will avoid disappointment. Putting hope in anything else can be unreliable and therefore the risks of a let-down are bound to be there. That doesn't mean to say we shouldn't hope for other things – it would be silly not to do so. But if we do, we need to maintain a measure of reality and remember that the answers are not guaranteed.

These are the eight things which the Bible says we can put our hope in, with complete assurance:

1. God's unfailing love (Ps 33:18).
2. God's grace and help in times of trouble (Ps 71:1–5, 13–14 and Heb 13:6).
3. A future when earthly suffering will end (Rom 8:20–25 and Rev 21:4). There are no guarantees of this happening in the present. Quite the reverse – Jesus promises us trouble while we are in the world!
4. An eternal house in heaven (2 Cor 5:1–5 and 2 Pet 3:13).
5. Meeting Jesus in the rapture (1 Thess 4:13–18).
6. Receiving crowns from God: a crown of righteousness (2 Tim 4:8) and a crown of glory (1 Pet 5:4).
7. Eternal life (Titus 1:2, 3:7).
8. God's word. The writer of the epic Psalm 119 says on at least three occasions, 'I have put my hope in your word.' We should do the same – it is breathed by God himself (2 Tim 3:16). Having said this, it is important to read it properly, as described in

Chapter 3, otherwise let-downs will sometimes follow.

This list should be comprehensive enough to satisfy every one of us, since it offers assurance both for our present and our future. In our modern world it is easy for us to yearn for more tangible things. If we do, then disappointment and broken-heartedness will inevitably follow, for as Christians we are spiritual beings and should always have our primary focus on the spiritual rather than the physical.

The disappointments in a here-and-now kingdom

Over the last twenty years, considerable attention has been placed on the fact that we can enjoy God's kingdom on earth now, rather than wait for it at some point in the future. This is not wrong. The Bible makes it very clear that the kingdom of God can and should be a present reality. Jesus prayed that his Father's kingdom would come *on earth*. Hebrews 12:28 says we are *receiving* a kingdom which cannot be shaken, and Colossians 1:13 emphasises that God has *brought* us into the kingdom of his Son. These scriptures indicate that the kingdom *is* something we can see, taste and experience now. But to focus too heavily on this concept is a quick route to a broken heart. For the Bible says far more about the kingdom of God's *future* aspect. And so although we have to live with the often confusing tension of a kingdom now *and* the kingdom to come, our primary focus should be on a certain, eternal future, not an unreliable and unpredictable present.

Previous generations have probably placed a greater emphasis on the kingdom to come, and this resulted in many Christians sitting around, helpless and beleaguered by life, waiting for Jesus to come and carry out an SAS-style rescue one day at the Second Coming. How tragic! There has to be more to Christian life than this! However, placing too much emphasis on kingdom is now causing, and will continue to cause, enormous discouragement. For I do not believe it is possible to establish God's kingdom on earth to the extent that many people believe, and it is foolish to place our hope in a concept which is by no means certain.

In spiritual warfare, some pray as though the enemy can be rendered completely powerless and that unrighteousness can be utterly blotted out in each and every situation. If we believe this can happen, then we are fooling ourselves and showing an alarming ignorance of Scripture.

For 2 Timothy 3:1–5 spells out an alarming picture for God's people living in the end times. Paul tells his young disciple:

> But mark this: There will be terrible times in the last days. People will be lovers of themselves, lovers of money, boastful, proud, abusive, disobedient to their parents, ungrateful, unholy, without love, unforgiving, slanderous, without self-control, brutal, not lovers of the good, treacherous, rash, conceited, lovers of pleasure rather than lovers of God . . .

Jesus gave similar warnings. He told his disciples in Matthew 24:12 that there would be an increase in wickedness during the end times; and that those days would be like the days of Noah (Lk 17:26), where evil was running out of control; and the days of Lot (Lk 17:28) when perversion and homosexuality were rife to the extent that not even angels were safe.

We need to keep these warnings well in mind when we pray for and dream about establishing God's kingdom on the earth. Yes that kingdom can and will be established. But it will be alongside an increasing tide of sin and wickedness, not instead of it. This means that even though Satan is a defeated foe, his influence and destruction on society is likely to increase, not abate.

God's total rule and direct judgement will not happen until the end of the age when, as we are told in Revelation 19:15, Jesus will rule the nations with an iron sceptre and cast the devil into the lake of sulphur (Rev 20:10). Paul describes the scene clearly in 1 Corinthians 15:24–25: 'Then the end will come, when he hands over the kingdom to God the Father after he has destroyed all dominion, authority and power. For he must reign until he has put all his enemies under his feet.' Although they are defeated, they are not there yet.

Similarly, those who are rightly involving themselves in green issues and the care of our planet can never expect to see the earth properly restored to its Eden-like state, because it is under a curse (Gen 3:17). And according to Revelation 21:1 and 22:3 this curse will only disappear when the existing heavens and earth pass away. To hope for more is again guaranteeing disappointment and a lot of hard work with little return.

We will only maintain a positive attitude if we can grasp the fact that although Jesus wants us to begin establishing his kingdom now, he does not want us to finish the job! That is for him to do, and if we think we can accomplish things now which he has determined will happen in the future, then we will end up becoming very discouraged. Expecting God's kingdom to come immediately is nothing new – see Luke 19:11. But Jesus made it clear this was not the case.

Yes, we should be seeking God's kingdom, his presence and his power in our lives with every ounce of zeal and enthusiasm that we can muster. But the balance of our hope and faith should be in the future glory, not glory now. For our ultimate future is eternal, and consequently we need to be storing up spiritual treasure in heaven, where it matters, not on earth, which will eventually pass away.

Taking towns for God

I've lost count of how many prayer meetings I have been to where people pray along the lines of 'We're going to take Mugthorpe for God.' And I always wonder exactly what people mean by that. My experience is that some people are praying for things which the Bible never says will happen.

I have no doubts that we can pray that revival will break out in Mugthorpe, that people will become Christians, that righteousness will be established, churches united, lives and situations changed and the spiritual climate of the town changed. God can and will answer faith-filled, persistent prayers like this. But I do not believe it is possible to see God, his church or his kingdom established in a town to the extent that some people hope for and pray for. To expect the supreme here-and-now reign of Jesus in our towns and nations is to fail to understand Jesus' victory over Satan.

It is true that Jesus came to destroy the devil's work

(1 Jn 3:8) and achieved a total victory over Satan and all his forces of darkness. But, as the writer to the Hebrews put it, 'In putting everything under him, God left nothing that is not subject to him. *Yet at present we do not see everything subject to him. But we see Jesus* . . .' (2:8–9, my italics). In other words, even though Jesus' victory over the devil is complete, it is not realistic to expect to see the *enforcement* of that victory in every situation. And on the occasions when it is not enforced, Jesus is no less victorious and our hope must rest in him, crowned with glory; the Jesus who will finally enforce his rule at the end of the age (Rev 19:14–16).

The apostle Paul and his team made the most extraordinary impact on Europe and parts of Asia, and saw massive revivals and spiritual upheaval in virtually every town they went to. They planted powerful, effective churches that were clearly dynamic in spiritual warfare. But history shows that those churches in places like Corinth, Ephesus and Thessalonica and many other places besides never achieved complete victory over their spiritual enemies. Far from it. Neither will we – or at least, not until Jesus comes again.

Next time you hear someone say, or pray, that they are going to take their town for God, ask them what they mean. You may well discover they are anticipating a lot more than Jesus ever promised, and are setting themselves up for significant disappointment.

Seeing the bigger picture

It is so easy for us to be so caught up with our busy lifestyles and the task of fulfilling the Great Commission on earth that we forget that we are meant to be people like Abraham, who is described as an alien and a stranger on earth. It is so important that our hearts are impregnated with the bigger picture that God has for us; a picture that goes beyond our lives and beyond this earth and stretches into heaven and into eternity.

Yes, your life here and now is important and has significance. You only get one go at it and there aren't any rehearsals! But the things you are going through and hoping for now are only a tiny piece of a huge jigsaw, and to see it any other way means you will place your priorities on the wrong things.

Abraham lived on earth, but only started to see God's kingdom established there. He was looking forward 'to the city with foundations, whose architect and builder is God' (Heb 11:10). He knew that the land God promised him was not the end of his pilgrimage – he was just travelling through, on his way to something much bigger. This is what kept him going during the trials of his life and the testing of his faith. He saw a bigger picture. Hebrews 11:16 says he was longing for a better country, a heavenly one. We should be doing the same. We should be so fired up and consumed with the prospect of reigning with Jesus after his Second Coming, of an eternal future with him and his Father in heaven, that earthly activities will pale into insignificance and disappointments will not hit us so hard. While we continue to focus too strongly on establishing a kingdom now, we will find it hard to recover from knocks, because we will carry on expecting a lot – and not receiving all of it. It is better if we can learn not to expect to receive all of God's promises now and to try to understand that the things we are experiencing and receiving at the moment, whether good or bad, are just a tiny taste of an incredible tomorrow. In this way we will always remain hungry for more and avoid hope being deferred.

The heroes of faith in Hebrews 11 did not, we are told, receive the things promised. 'They only saw them and welcomed them from a distance' (Heb 11:13). Many of the things we pray and hope for now are, I believe, things that we have glimpsed and are welcoming from a distance. So we need to hold on to them lightly and with the realisation that while we may see them come to fruition now, the chances are that we may not – they are things to yearn for in heaven.

Ultimately the only way we will keep our hope, our health and our sanity in this confusing post-modern era is to focus firmly on our eternal future, on spiritual things and on Jesus himself. They are the only things that are reliable. They will never break our hearts.

The two disciples hurried back along the road from Emmaus to Jerusalem just as fast as they could. Gone were the doubts, the tears and the disappointments which had tormented them earlier that day. This time their tread was light and the miles passed by quickly in the cool of the early evening.

And there were no awkward silences this time, either. The two men's conversation was animated as they discussed the day's strange events, culminating with their startling recognition of Jesus over a meal in an old stone lodging house, often used as a resting place by merchants and traders, on the outskirts of Emmaus. Once the two men had realised who Jesus was, they hadn't wasted any

more time. No more isolation for them! They left
Emmaus straight away and went back to Jerusalem to
find their friends before it got too dark to undertake
the seven-mile journey.

They arrived back in the bustling city just as it was
growing dark. Lights were beginning to twinkle in the
windows of some of the homes and there was the usual
clamour of noise everywhere: the crying of babies, the
braying of donkeys and the babble of traders and
merchants. The two men looked at one another uneasily.
There were patrols of Roman soldiers everywhere,
enforcing an uneasy peace after the mayhem of Jesus'
crucifixion just days earlier. Jerusalem still wasn't the
place for followers of Jesus to be seen in public. They
kept their heads down as they hurried through the
winding streets, wrinkling their noses at the peculiar
blend of smells ... animal dung, aromatic spices and
the pungent odour of men smoking hashish.

They had no doubt that the other disciples were still in
hiding, and since none of them came from Jerusalem,
there was only one place they could be. That was at the
home of the lady called Mary, who had let Jesus and the
twelve disciples use her guest room for the Passover
supper just days earlier. After a brisk walk for several
minutes, they arrived at the big house, looked cautiously
around them and then knocked quietly on the door.

A young man called John Mark, Mary's son, opened
the door a crack and immediately recognised Cleopas
and his friend. 'Quickly, come in,' he breathed, and
ushered the men inside.

The three men hurried up the stairs and went into the
room. Cleopas gasped when he saw how many people

were there! Not just the eleven remaining disciples, but a large number of Jesus' other friends and followers too, all chattering quietly but excitedly about the risen Jesus. 'Yes,' said some of the disciples. 'The Lord is indeed risen and has appeared to Simon.'

The room grew quiet and Cleopas and his friend began to describe what had happened to them on the Emmaus road that day. There were gasps of excitement and cries of 'Praise the Lord' as their story unfolded.

The healing process, which began when Jesus sought them out, was complete. Their minds had been renewed and their hearts ignited again with Scripture. They had been given a vibrant new revelation of Jesus. And now they were back where they should be – among their brothers, sisters and friends.

Jesus still uses the same methods to heal his broken-hearted believers today. He seeks us out and, in time, inspires us once again with the truth of his word and a fresh revelation of himself.

The Emmaus road is one that is full of tears, loneliness and shattered dreams. It's a dry, difficult place.

But it's not a one-way journey. You can come back – refreshed, revived, and keen to see your friends again.

Holidaying in Sri Lanka with her father, Cordelia met Marcus Stone—and it didn't take her long to fall deeply in love with him. But did Marcus really return her feelings? Or should Cordelia believe the beautiful Sri Lankan girl Sugin, who claimed that she herself was so much more than Marcus's 'housekeeper'?

THE LION ROCK

BY

SALLY WENTWORTH

MILLS & BOON LIMITED
15–16 BROOK'S MEWS
LONDON W1A 1DR

First published 1983
Australian copyright 1983
Philippine copyright 1983
This edition 1983

© Sally Wentworth 1983

ISBN 0 263 74424 8

Set in Monophoto Times 11 on 11 pt.
01–1283 – 54015

Made and printed in Great Britain by
Richard Clay (The Chaucer Press) Ltd,
Bungay, Suffolk

CHAPTER ONE

THE view from the hotel balcony was breathtaking. It looked out over a deep green valley rich with strange and exotic trees, many of them tall coconut palms that whispered in the light breeze. Small white houses, roofed with woven palm leaves, dotted the hillsides and grew thicker on the lower ground where they clustered round the ornate, pink-walled temple just visible through the trees. The temple stood alongside the still green waters of a lake built by an ancient king for his queen, but where, on an island in the centre and connected to the palace by an underground passage, the king maintained his harem of beautiful concubines. Across the lake the land rose again, the greenery giving way to the misty greyness of rock as the hills peaked against the clear azure sky.

Cordelia Allingham breathed a long sigh of pleasure, her soft blue eyes drinking in every detail of the scene. The scent of flowers stole towards her and for a fleeting moment she thought she found something familiar in the fragrance, but then it was gone, no matter how hard she tried to retrieve the memory. The sun was hot on her bare arms, even though it was quite late in the afternoon, and she stepped back into the shadow of a gabled roof overhung with dark red pantiles and sat down in a rattan chair. She was tired from the long journey but was much too enthralled by the scenery before her to go and rest. And excited too, excited at the thought of coming home, although even now she could hardly believe that she was really here in Sri Lanka, this beautiful island that hung like a jewelled earring from the mainland of India.

Or rather, back here, because she had been born in Sri Lanka just over twenty years ago. Only it had been called Ceylon then, and had been part of the British Commonwealth, not a republic as it was today. Not that she remembered a great deal of the country from her childhood, as she'd been sent back to boarding school in England when she was only seven and had spent all her holidays with an aunt, her mother's sister, who lived near Bath, because she was too young to travel so far alone. But then when Cordelia was about eleven her mother had joined her in England, leaving her father behind, and had never gone back.

Cordelia's memories of those years were vague, she had pushed them to the back of her mind as one tends to do with memories that hurt or are unpleasant; she only remembered vividly one incident, when her father had come home on leave from his job and there had been a terrible row because her mother refused to leave England and go back with him. He had always been a man of violent temper, and he had stormed out of the house. Neither of them saw him again until Cordelia's mother died when she was fifteen and he had turned up at the funeral. By then he was again living in England, working in a London office and hating every minute of it, his job as the manager of a huge tea estate in Sri Lanka lost when all the tea plantations were nationalised by the government of the new republic. So many years had passed without any contact that by then they were strangers, neither of them able to bridge the gap of age or apprehension. Her father had tried, clumsily, but Cordelia had been feeling too deeply the loss of her mother's love and support to do anything but coldly and instantly reject an offer of the same from anyone else. So they had gone their separate ways again with only the dutiful exchange of cards at Christmas to acknowledge any kind of relationship.

A noise from the next room along penetrated her thoughts and made her look at her watch. She'd been sitting dreaming on the balcony so long that it was time to change for dinner. Hastily she went back into her room and took off the jeans and shirt she'd worn to travel in from London. It had been a long journey: a fourteen-hour flight with refuelling stops in Zurich and Dubai, and then a two-and-a-half-hour drive from Colombo airport inland up into the hills to this hotel near the town of Kandy which they were to make their base. She had been worried about her father and had tried to persuade him to stay in Colombo overnight, but he had insisted on pushing on, saying that he wanted to get the worst of the travelling over and done with. Just as he had insisted that they have dinner as soon as the dining-room opened so that they could get a good night's sleep and make an early start in the morning.

Tucking her long fair hair into a shower cap, Cordelia turned on the taps of the rather ancient-looking shower and was pleasantly surprised when warm water came through. She stepped under it, wondering if her father was all right. Her father! She shook her head in puzzlement, amazed that she was really here with him. It had all happened so quickly. He had just suddenly turned up on the doorstep of the flat she shared with three other girls one day, and more or less demanded that she go with him on this trip. At first she hadn't recognised him; he seemed to have grown old since the last time she had seen him, his brown hair had turned grey and there were new lines on his face, his skin that had once had the tan of years spent in the hot sun, looked yellow and unhealthy. He had always been a big, hefty man, but now his flesh seemed to cling to bones that were too heavy for him so that his shoulders bent under the weight.

He said that he had been ill, that he wanted to go back to Sri Lanka to convalesce, but his doctor wouldn't let him go unless he had someone with him to take care of him.

Cordelia's first emotion had been one of pity when she saw how he had changed, but his brusque manner had almost immediately hardened her feelings. She had suggested he hire a trained nurse to take care of him, but this he had bluntly refused to do, saying that he was well enough, he only wanted someone to organise things for him, that he didn't really want or need a companion at all and it was only a sop to his doctor. Cordelia could well believe it and she had argued against going with him, pointing out that she had a job and couldn't take indefinite leave and that she was taking a course of evening classes. But he had bludgeoned down all her arguments with a wave of his clenched fist, a gesture she remembered from long ago. She could give up her job and he would pay all her expenses and her share of the rent of the flat while she was away. She could take her books with her and study while she was in Sri Lanka, and join the class again when she got back.

But even then she wouldn't have gone with him,

not just for his sake, and they had grown too far apart for her to feel any old-fashioned sense of duty towards him. No, she had agreed in the end only because she couldn't resist the opportunity to go back to the land of her birth, to see again in reality those dim memories of a land of sun and long white beaches, of brilliant flowers and endless seas.

Slipping on a short-sleeved cotton dress, Cordelia applied fresh make-up and tidied her hair. Seven-fifteen; she still had a quarter of an hour in hand. She knocked at her father's door but there was no reply; he must already have gone down. All the rooms on this storey of the hotel opened on to a stone-floored gallery with a white-painted balustrade. Going to the edge, Cordelia looked down and saw a pool with flamboyantly coloured fish darting among the pieces of lacy coral and the stems of lotus flowers, then she looked up and smiled delightedly; the well of the gallery had no roof, it was open to the evening sky.

She went on down the wide staircase and found her father sitting in the bar, a drink on the low table in front of him, a cigarette between his fingers. Cordelia crossed to sit in a chair opposite him.

'Would you like a drink?'

'Yes, please. A Bacardi and Coke.'

James Allingham raised a hand and beckoned imperiously to the bar waiter. He came over immediately; he was wearing a white jacket over a blue and black patterned sarong and he had plastic flip-flops on his feet. 'Yes, sir?' he asked with a wide smile on his brown face.

'A Bacardi and Coke and another gin and tonic,' her father said shortly.

'Does your doctor allow you to drink—and smoke?' Cordelia asked tentatively as the waiter hurried away.

'I'll do as I damn well like,' he answered curtly, his jaw thrusting forward obstinately.

Cordelia looked at him for a moment, then settled back in her seat. Well, if he wanted to make himself ill again what right had she got to interfere? And as she didn't particularly enjoy having her head bitten off every time she tried to show concern, then he could go ahead and do what he liked for all she cared.

The waiter came up with the drinks and Cordelia smiled and thanked him, getting a big smile in return. Her father didn't even bother to look up as his drink was put in front of him and the empty glass taken away. His attitude continued during dinner; Cordelia noticed that he was extremely short with the waiters, who were mostly young and very willing, although not speaking very fluent English. He never said please or thank you to them and got very impatient if they didn't understand what he wanted straightaway.

'The main language here is Sinhalese, isn't it?' Cordelia asked to fill the silence while they waited for their soup. He nodded and she went on, 'Didn't you learn to speak it while you were living here?'

'Yes, of course I did,'

'Why don't you use it, then?'

James Allingham gave a short, bitter laugh. 'These peasants are supposed to be running what they laughingly describe as a tourist hotel. If they want tourists to come here they must learn to speak their language. I certainly don't intend to pander to their laziness by helping them out.'

The soup came and Cordelia ate hers, wondering if her father had always been this bitter and bad-tempered or whether his illness had changed him. She could remember him being hot-tempered, but that was a far cry from this continuous sourness. If he had been like this all the time, then it was no wonder that her mother had left him; Cordelia could only marvel that she had stopped with him as long as she had. He must be getting on for sixty now, Cordelia reckoned; he hadn't married until his late thirties and his wife had been almost fifteen years younger.

There weren't many other people in the dining-room; it was August and the off-season for this part of the island, so they were served quickly and soon finished their meal. Cordelia would have liked to go for a walk to stretch her legs, but it was already dark outside and she didn't fancy going alone in case she got lost; the hotel had seemed to be situated among a maze of narrow, unmade-up roads when they had arrived, and there weren't any street lights. One glance at the lines of tiredness around her father's eyes decided her against asking him to go with her, and anyway, a few moments later he stood up and announced that he was going to turn in.

'I've already arranged for a car for tomorrow,' he informed her. 'You'll need to be down for breakfast at seven-thirty and we'll leave at eight.'

Anger at his high-handedness almost made her retort that she would get up when she damn well liked, but then she shrugged mentally; after all, he was paying for this trip, so she supposed he had a right to say when they would travel, but he could certainly be a bit more polite about it! She nodded briefly and rose to follow him upstairs. At his door they merely exchanged a brief goodnight and Cordelia went on to her own room. But she didn't immediately get ready for bed, instead she went to sit out on the balcony again and listened to the sounds of the night: to the dogs who had lain supine in the sun all day and only now came alive to fill the air with their howling, to the constant chirp of tree frogs, and the distant rattle of a train. And now that tantalising scent came back to her more strongly, a faint spicy muskiness, and at last the memory returned: it was the smell of Sri Lanka, the land of her birth, and the only thing that had stayed with her over the years she had been away. Suddenly her heart surged with emotion and she was filled with a sense of peace and satisfaction, the knowledge that she had come home.

The car her father had ordered was waiting for them outside the entrance of the hotel punctually next morning. It was a large black car which looked as if it had seen better days. Beside it stood a smartly dressed Sri Lankan driver.

'Good morning, sir. Good morning, madam.' He rushed to open the rear door for them.

'We don't need you,' James Allingham told him. 'I only ordered a car, not a driver.'

'Oh, but sir,' the man started to protest, 'to a stranger these roads can be very dangerous. It is better if I drive you.'

'I'm no stranger,' her father informed him tersely. He turned impatiently to Cordelia, who was looking at the two men uncertainly. 'Come on, get in the passenger seat.'

She tried to compromise. 'Why don't I drive?'

He laughed shortly. 'Not on these roads. You'd have an accident within the first mile.' When she still hesitated, he added brusquely, 'I drove myself around this island for over twenty years and I'm quite capable of doing it now!'

Cordelia realised that there was no point in arguing, and got into the front seat hoping that he was fit enough to drive. It would help if she knew what his illness had been but when she had asked he had just shrugged off the question.

'There isn't much point in my being here if you won't let me do anything,' she pointed out rather tartly.

James Allingham looked at her coldly for a moment, then started the car. Cordelia felt completely snubbed.

Their hotel gripped the steep hillside overlooking the town of Kandy, and they were soon caught up in the early morning traffic making its way into the centre of the town. Everyone drove on the left, the same as in England, but this seemed to be the only piece of organisation among the general chaos. The road was thronged not only with cars, but also with ancient Mercedes buses, painted red and grey, all of them with scrapes and torn metal along their sides, and all of them so crammed full of people that they bulged out of the doorway, hanging on by one hand or on to someone else who had a better hold. There were slow bullock carts loaded with fruit or vegetables for the market, literally hundreds of people on bicycles as well as a few motorbikes and the smart mini-coaches used for tourist excursions. Everyone drove on their horns, so that the air was filled with the shrill cacophony, but the crowds of pedestrians who overflowed the pavements on to the road seemed to take no notice at all, only moving out of the way at the very last moment.

Cordelia decided that they must have built in radar or something, and she sighed in relief as an old man moved out of the way when she'd been sure that they were going to run him down. Her father had been quite right, she realised; she would never have been confident to drive through this lot, but he seemed quite unperturbed, even had a slight grin of enjoyment on his face.

Beyond the town the traffic thinned out a little, although the roads grew progressively worse and she was bounced around in her seat as they drove over ridges and potholes. Her father still sounded the horn peremptorily whenever another vehicle or some people on foot got in the way, but Cordelia had time to take in the passing scenery: the paddy fields where women cut the rice by hand, the working elephants moving huge sawn tree-trunks, the tiny open-fronted shops in the villages that sold strange fruit and vegetables and yellow king-coconuts for thirsty travellers to drink.

She had brought her camera with her and would have liked to stop a dozen times to take photographs, but her father took little notice of the scenery and seemed intent to push on. After a couple of hours' driving the road began to rise, running in big hairpin bends among steep hills that were planted with thousands of low, evenly cut green bushes clinging to hillsides that looked too steep for anything but a mountain goat to walk on.

'There are the first of the tea plantations,' James Allingham told her.

'Is this where we used to live?'

'No, the old Braemar plantation is some miles farther on in the best soil area.'

Sri Lanka seemed to be full of people, even out here there were men walking barefoot along the side of the road, and women washing themselves or their clothes under one of the small waterfalls that cascaded over the grey rocks, and there were small children with bunches of exotic wild flowers in their hands who tried to attract their attention so that they would stop and buy the flowers from them.

The road rose higher and the hairpins became sharper until, at the top of one very steep hill, her father pulled off the main road and stopped outside a huge grey building that dominated the landscape.

'Here we are,' he said. 'This is the Braemar tea factory.'

He didn't get out of the car straight away, but sat looking round, and Cordelia tactfully stayed silent. Obviously the place was bringing back memories for him, but she was disappointed to find that she could remember nothing of the place. After a few minutes he gave a sort of grunt of dissatisfaction and got slowly out of the car, Cordelia following. The day was really starting to get hot, even so high up where a breeze came off the hills. She was wearing only a sundress but already she was beginning to feel the heat. There was a sort of courtyard outside the factory with, on the far side, a low, newish-looking building with 'Tourist Reception' written on the door. James Allingham grunted disgustedly when he saw this and walked straight towards the entrance to the factory, completely ignoring it.

As they approached the door, however, a girl in a green sari came out of the tourist office and ran after them. 'Please, you wish to see the factory? I will take you.'

Her father turned and eyed the girl with thinly-veiled contempt. 'I don't need some girl to take me round. I know the workings of this place better than you ever will.'

The girl's smile stayed on her face. 'Oh, but sir, it is not allowed that you go alone. I must take you.'

He snorted angrily. 'Come, if you must, but I'll do my own tour.'

Taking a firm hold of Cordelia's elbow, he led her into the cool shade of the factory and started to tell her how the tea was processed, climbing up steep flights of stairs that were more like ladders, to the upper floors where the drying racks were and then down again to see the more mechanised part of the operation and finally to the white-tiled testing room where the different grades of tea were tasted. By this time he was puffing a bit and there were patches of colour on his cheeks.

Trying to keep any sign of concern out of her voice, Cordelia said carefully, 'Looking at that tea makes me feel thirsty; is there somewhere where we could try it?'

The guide had followed them all round, hovering in the background, and now she said, 'Oh, yes. We offer cups of tea to our visitors in the tourist centre. Or there is a place outside if you prefer it.'

'We'll take it outside.'

They walked out and sat under the shade of a circular, thatched-roof building that was open on all sides. It looked out over the deep valleys and steep hills of the tea plantations, the colour of the bushes giving the hills a uniform green appearance. Cordelia sat with the sun hot on her back and wished her father would stop going on about the lack of improvements that had taken place since his time. 'They've hardly brought in any mechanisation,' he was saying disparagingly. 'They could treble their rate of production and packing if they used modern methods. Too many of the processes are still done by hand.'

'How big did you say this island is—about the size of Scotland?' Cordelia asked him.

'About that.'

'And there are over fifteen million people living here?'

'Yes.'

'Then,' she pointed out reasonably, 'perhaps it's better for them not to be mechanised. If they brought in machines they would throw thousands of people out of work and the state would have to keep them out of the extra profit they made from the tea factories. It's a Catch 22 type situation.'

James Allingham looked at her coldly. 'And since when have you become an economics expert?' he demanded sneeringly.

A flash of anger shone in Cordelia's eyes, but she was prevented from making the sharp retort that came to her lips by the return of the guide with a tray with cups of tea of different grades for them to try. The girl fussed over them, still polite and smiling despite her father's rudeness. He asked her if they still had the records of people who had worked at the plantation and seemed more put out than the answer warranted when the girl said that they only kept the records for three years. When they had tried the tea, which he pronounced as 'inferior quality rubbish', he turned to the girl and told her that he wanted to see round the manager's bungalow.

'But that is a private house,' the girl protested.

'Nevertheless I want to see it. I was the manager

of this place myself before it was stolen from the rightful owners by your government. I used to live in the manager's house and my daughter was born there. I want her to see it.'

'Oh, no, please,' Cordelia protested. 'It may not be convenient.'

'Then they'll have to make it convenient,' her father snapped. 'I didn't come all the way here to be fobbed off by some native girl!'

Cordelia flushed with embarrassment and walked away from him. If she hadn't she would really have let go and told him just what she thought of his boorish manners. The door of the tourist centre was open and she went in. There were some other people there, sitting around drinking the tea, enjoying their holiday. Cordelia was beginning to wish she'd never come. She bought a few packets of the best grade tea to take back as presents, but her mind wasn't really on it, she was just wondering how she was going to get through the rest of their visit here without losing her temper.

The next hour was as bad as Cordelia expected it to be. They had to wait some time until the girl came and said they could go to the bungalow, her father growing more impatient by the minute, and he ruined any enjoyment she might have found in seeing the house where she was born. The wife of the present manager, whose home and privacy he was invading, he treated as if she was some usurper who was trespassing in a house that still belonged to him. He pointed out to Cordelia things that had been added since his time and spoke loudly and disparagingly of the alterations. 'These people are little more than peasants,' he informed her. 'They don't know what civilised standards are.'

Cordelia bit her lip and somehow held on to her temper, knowing that to lose it in front of strangers would only make things worse. The manager's wife was obviously puzzled and upset by his attitude, but she remained unfailingly polite, even offering them more tea and cakes which James Allingham brusquely refused. They looked round the garden, which Cordelia thought was lovely, but in whose flowers and beautiful, exotic trees he could only find a poor comparison, and then, to her relief, they left. But, to add insult to rudeness, as they went out he gave the poor woman only a cursory word of thanks and dropped a twenty-rupee note on to a table as a tip. Cordelia hadn't remembered the bungalow, but she thought she would never forget the look on that woman's face as long as she lived.

She managed to control her feelings until they were back in the car and driving away, but then she turned to face her father and said furiously, 'How could you behave so rudely? Just because you happened to be the manager of that plantation once it doesn't give you the right to treat the people there now like dirt, does it? And to throw down money for that woman after you'd barged your way into her home—it was . . .' her anger almost choked her, 'it was disgusting!'

Her father glared at her. 'Who the hell do you think you're talking to? And just what do you think you know about these people? They're just one generation removed from peasants and they have to be kept in their place. And they never do anything unless it's for money. You'll soon find that out. They're a greedy, lazy rabble, the lot of them!'

'The ones I've met have been polite and friendly enough.' Cordelia started to argue back, but he turned on her and shouted her down. He started to get very red in the face and the car swerved wildly as he took a corner too fast and swung it back on to the road. A car coming the other way hooted furiously and Cordelia remembered that he'd been ill. Gripping her hands into tight fists, she forced herself to sit in silence and not answer back, her mouth pressed grimly shut, and eventually James Allingham calmed down a little, although he still drove too fast in angry defiance of her criticism.

They had lunch at the Hill Club in Nuwara Eliya. The town had been built during the British occupancy as a hill station and looked like any English town—it even had a golf course and a racecourse. The Hill Club was a large building of grey stone that looked rather like an English manor house in the Cotswolds except for the statues of lions on either side of the entrance portico and the elephant's foot umbrella stand in the hallway. They had a drink in the bar before going into the large, polished oak dining-room where lunch was served to them by very correct waiters in white jackets and sarongs. Cordelia stuck to food she recognised, but her father asked for curry, insisting on having it very hot. He drank a lot of beer to go with it, several times asking for his glass to be refilled.

Afterwards they had coffee, but James Allingham was soon on his feet again. 'I want to drive round the town before we go back,' he said eagerly.

Cordelia followed him willingly enough; he had seemed more at ease at the Hill Club, a place that he had frequented during his time in Sri Lanka and which had remained much the same. But the changes that had taken place in the town brought his anger flooding back.

'Look at that!' he pointed out furiously. 'They've turned one of the best homes around into a damned hotel!' And he complained about other places that had been neglected. 'They've let the whole place go to rack and ruin. I bet nobody's lifted a finger since we were here to stand over them and tell them what to do all the time.' He slammed his fist down angrily on the steering wheel. 'They've even closed the bloody racecourse!'

Abruptly he turned the car and started driving fast out of the town. 'I'm getting out of this place! I should never have come back here.'

They went back the same way as they had come, along the road that climbed up into the hills and snaked along in steep hairpin bends.

'Oh, look!' Cordelia exclaimed. 'Those two little boys with the flowers are racing us by running straight down the hillside while we go round by the road.' She watched and laughed delightedly when the two boys arrived panting on the lower road and looked at them with expectant grins as they drove up. Her father drove right by without even glancing at them, but the boys plunged gamely across the road and down the path while the car went round the next hairpin. The boys were there ahead of them again on the lower level, both panting for breath. 'There they are. Stop a minute so that I can give them something.'

But James Allingham drove straight on again.

'Why didn't you stop?' Cordelia asked in surprise and disappointment.

'I'm not encouraging those kids. There are enough of them begging from tourists and making nuisances of themselves already.'

The two boys started to run down to the next stretch of road and Cordelia, her patience snapping, said tartly, 'I don't know why you wanted to come back here when you obviously hate the place and the people so much. Or is it that you're just a masochist?'

'Don't try and pin labels on me, girl,' her father returned angrily. 'Especially when you don't know what the hell you're talking about!'

'Then why did you come back? You obviously aren't enjoying yourself, and you're rude to the people even though they're very friendly and . . .'

'That's the trouble,' James Allingham shouted in sudden vehement anger. 'They're too bloody friendly! Always smiling at you and talking to you and making you feel that you want to get to know them. You have to keep them at a distance, do you hear me? You have to push them away before they get too close!'

He was shouting at her now and had gone red in the face. To Cordelia's horror he suddenly began to clutch at his collar, beads of sweat grew on his forehead and he started to make great gasping noises as if he couldn't get his breath.

'Dad!' Cordelia cried out in fear and horror as he held both hands to his chest and gave a great cry of agony, then he slumped forward, falling across the steering wheel.

'Dad! Dad!' She screamed in terror, realising that the car was running out of control. Desperately she grabbed the wheel, but her father's weight made it impossible to steer and he was too heavy for her to push out of the way. They were going downhill, approaching the next hairpin and the steep drop down the hillside. Acting by pure instinct, Cordelia grabbed the handbrake and jerked it on. The car slowed but didn't stop because her father's foot was still on the accelerator. With a sob of despair, she threw herself down and reached across to push his foot off the pedal, then she put both hands on the footbrake and rammed it down as hard as she could go. The car slowed, came to a stop, and for a wonderful moment she thought that they were safe, but then it teetered and slid over the edge, falling on its side as it careered down the hillside.

Curled up as she was on the floor, Cordelia wasn't thrown about too much, she hung on to the gear lever, but her left hip was banged repeatedly against what was now the floor and once her arm came up against something sharp and she cried out in pain. Her father fell down across the seat and was partly lying on top of her. His eyes were closed and he seemed quite unconscious. For a few paralysing minutes, as the car plunged on, and Cordelia was crushed under his weight, she thought that he was dead. Then, after what seemed like an eternity, the car seemed to hit a harder surface, it rocked and then came to a standstill. Tentatively, almost forcing herself to do so, she managed to free one arm and put her hand on her father's chest. Faintly she felt it move, felt him breathing.

The two little boys with the flowers were the first to reach them. They climbed on the car and wrenched open the door, talking at the tops of their voices in a language she didn't understand. They were too small to help, but soon they came back with some men, workers on the tea estates. It took four of them to lift her father out and Cordelia got trodden on more than once as she was still pinned underneath. When it was her turn to be pulled out, she found that her legs wouldn't support her. She collapsed on to the grass and knelt there trembling. Looking around, she saw the great swathe that the car had cut through the undergrowth growing on the hillside until it had come to rest on a lower section of the road just before the hairpin. They had been lucky; she had managed to slow the car enough so that it just slid down instead of speeding over the edge and hurtling down from one level to the next all the way down the hill.

Quite a crowd had gathered round them now. A brightly painted lorry loaded with coconut fibre had stopped and the driver and his two passengers ran over and started shouting at the people who were standing round. Everyone was talking terribly loudly, waving their arms about and calling to others who seemed to appear from nowhere. They had laid her father on the grass and Cordelia crawled over to him. His face was grey and his breathing was very shallow. Several men and women were standing by him, but no one seemed to be *doing anything*.

She looked round wildly at the crowd of dark faces that stared at her so curiously. 'Please – somebody get an ambulance. Telephone for an ambulance!' Her plea came out on a high, hysterical note and for a moment the noise ceased as they all turned to stare at her. Then they all started talking volubly again, at her, at each other – and she couldn't understand a word.

'A doctor! You must get a doctor.' Cordelia staggered to her feet and only then became aware that her hip was terribly painful. Someone put out a hand to steady her, but she shook him off angrily. She pointed wildly at her father. 'He needs a doctor. Can't you understand? Where's the nearest telephone?'

But it was no use, they couldn't understand her, and even if they did, they had probably never used a telephone in their lives. She began to stagger along the road, reeling unsteadily, her head swimming, with some wild idea of walking to the nearest tea factory and using their phone to get help. Some men ran after her and caught hold of her, trying to pull her back, jabbering at her in Sinhalese. Tears of frustration ran down her cheeks. 'Leave me alone. I have to get help,' she muttered as she tried ineffectively to free herself.

Then she heard the sound of a car approaching and felt a great rush of hope as it came nearer and she saw a white man sitting in the front seat. It came to a stop and she somehow managed to shake off the hands that tried to restrain her and ran, limping, towards it. She reached it just as the door opened and a man stepped out. He was very tall and broad, and Cordelia's immediate impression of him was one of immeasurable strength. She almost fell against him and he caught hold of her, easily supporting her weight.

'What is it?' he asked sharply, his voice deep and wonderfully English.

'It's my father—he's hurt! The car crashed. Oh, help me, please help me!' she begged him, her eyes, dark with fear and panic, looking desperately into his.

The Englishman turned his head to snap out an order to the person he was with, then turned back to her. 'Don't worry,' he said reassuringly. 'I'll take care of him.'

She had been right about his strength, it was

there in every hard line of his face, in every intonation of his voice. Fortunately she recognised it and placed herself within it, letting the shock and fear take its toll as she fainted into his arms.

CHAPTER TWO

WHEN she came round, Cordelia found that she was being carried along, her head resting against a man's chest. For a moment she stayed still, taking in the masculine smell of tangy aftershave and the feel of the cool, clean cotton of his shirt beneath her cheek. She knew where she was and what had happened, knew that it must be the Englishman who was carrying her, but her head felt strangely giddy and heavy and it took her a moment or two before she could lift her eyelids and raise her head enough to see the strong, clean line of his jaw level with her eyes.

He must have felt her move, because he bent his head to look at her. His eyes were a very clear blue-grey under rather heavy lids.

'So you're back with us,' he remarked. 'Is your leg paining you very much?'

'No, no, it's all right.' She answered rather dazedly, not sure whether or not she'd complained about her leg. 'My—my father?' She tried to lift her head and look round.

'Easy.' The man's arms tightened. 'We've already got him in the car.' He came to a stop and set her gently on her feet by the open front door of his car. 'Shall I lift you in or can you manage it yourself? I've felt your legs and you don't appear to have broken anything, but I expect you're bruised pretty badly.'

'No, I can manage.' Cordelia got into the car, trying not very successfully to stifle a wince of pain

27

from her hip. Her father was stretched across the back seat, his head supported by a slim, wiry native. He was still unconscious, but she could hear his breath coming in wheezing, loud pants as if something was restricting his chest.

The Englishman had gone round to the driver's side and got in beside her. Cordelia turned to him and said anxiously, 'Is he all right like that? Shouldn't we wait for an ambulance? I'm sure he'd be much more comfortable lying down.'

'I expect he would,' the stranger agreed rather wryly. 'Unfortunately there are no hospitals nearer than Nuwara Eliya, and it would take at least an hour for an ambulance to get here and then another hour back to the hospital. So I think it will be best if we go to my house instead. It's quite near, will only take us about ten minutes.'

He had started up the car while he had been speaking and drove gently along the rutted, twisting road. At the bottom of the hill, he turned off the main road into a narrower one for about a mile and then paused to sound the horn in front of a pair of tall gates which were almost immediately swung open from within by two men in native sarongs. The Englishman drove on between flowering shrubs and trees for another couple of hundred yards, then drew up outside a large, white-painted bungalow.

A native servant girl came out to meet him and was sent inside again to quickly prepare a bedroom. Cordelia got out, but could only keep out of the way and watch anxiously as they gently manoeuvred her father out of the car and carried him inside the house. She hobbled after them into a large, sunny sitting-room and sank into a chair, feeling completely useless, but quite sure that her father was in capable hands. She leant back in the seat, feeling suddenly sick and trembly. Her father had looked so white, so ill. Her hands began to shake and she closed her eyes tight to try and shut out the mental picture.

'Here, drink this.'

The Englishman was standing by her chair, holding out a glass. She hadn't heard him come in or pour out the drink.

'What is it?'

'Brandy.'

Slowly she reached out to take the glass, but her hand was shaking so much that he exclaimed and took her hand, holding it steady. His hand was very firm, his fingers closing over hers and holding them as she drank. The brandy made her cough and choke a little, but she felt a bit better afterwards.

'You're obviously not used to strong drink,' he remarked, taking back the empty glass. 'Now what are you trying to do?' he demanded as she began to pull herself to her feet.

'My father—I must go to him.'

She was pushed gently but firmly down again. 'He's in very good hands and there's nothing you can do. The doctor should be here any minute to look at him.'

'Doctor?'

'Yes, there's a medical team visiting one of the local tea plantations today and I've telephoned for the doctor. We were lucky that he happened to be in the neighbourhood . . .' He broke off at the sound of a car outside. 'This must be him now. Sit tight while I talk to him.'

He went away and Cordelia heard him greeting someone, then the voices faded as a door closed behind them. Leaning back in her chair, she looked round the large, comfortable room, which had one wall completely open to the garden and the cool breeze that came off the hills. The other walls were painted white, providing a stark background for the rich colours of several pictures and batik wall hangings. The furniture was rather ornate to Western eyes but was obviously of good quality and very comfortable. There was electricity too; there were lamps on some of the tables and a music centre on a unit against one wall. She had just begun to wonder who the owner was and what he was doing living in a remote part of Sri Lanka, when he came back into the room. Immediately she sat forward in the chair, looking at him with worried, apprehensive eyes.

He gave a quick, negative movement of his dark head. 'Nothing yet. It will probably take the doctor some time to examine him. He has a nurse with him, so I've been sent out of the way.' Hooking up a chair, he sat in it, took out a pack of cigarettes and offered her one.

Cordelia shook her head. 'No, thanks.' She shouldn't have done that, it made her head start to ache and she frowned in pain.

'Is your leg hurting you? Would you like to lie down?'

'No, I'll wait.' She remembered that he had said he had felt her leg to see if it was broken. He must have seen her limping. Cordelia looked at him and her cheeks felt hot suddenly at the thought of this stranger's hands on her.

Possibly he read something of her thoughts, because he said, 'Perhaps you'd like to tell me who you are—and how the accident happened. My name's Stone, by the way—Marcus Stone.'

For a second the name seemed to strike an elusive chord in her memory, but he was waiting for her to speak and she had no time to think about it. 'Ours is Allingham,' she supplied into the expectant silence. 'I'm Cordelia and my father is James. We're over here on holiday. We only arrived yesterday.' Her voice broke for a moment and Marcus Stone looked at her in quick concern, seemed about to speak, but she went on, 'My father used to work in Sri Lanka, on a tea plantation. He—he wanted to see it all again.' She hesitated, not even sure in her own mind that that was really why her father had come back. But what other reason could there be? Slowly she went on, 'We hired a car this morning to go to Nuwara Eliya. And then—and then on the way back he—he suddenly went all red in the face and collapsed over the wheel.' She shuddered, remembering.

'You say your father collapsed before the crash?'

His voice cut sharply through the horrific pictures in her mind, bringing her back to reality. She nodded dumbly.

'It may help the doctor to know that. I'll go and tell him.'

He was gone for longer this time and when he came back the doctor, a middle-aged Sri Lankan with thinning hair and a moustache, was with him.

'Miss—Allingham?' The doctor sat down on the chair Marcus Stone had vacated. 'Does your father have a heart condition?'

Cordelia shrugged helplessly. 'I'm afraid I don't know. You see, I haven't seen him for some time until quite recently. I know that he's been ill, but—well, he wouldn't tell me what had been wrong with him.'

Both men looked surprised at this statement. 'Could he have had a heart attack?'

'I'm sorry, I just don't know. I did ask him, but he just wouldn't tell me. He shrugged it off and said it hadn't been anything serious.'

'I see,' the doctor murmured, although he plainly didn't understand. Probably he thought it was just another example of foreign madness. 'Did you have a meal recently?'

'Why, yes,' Cordelia answered in surprise. 'At the Hill Club in Nuwara Eliya.'

'And I suppose you had curry?'

'My father did. I just had an omelette.'

'Did he ask for it very hot?'

'Yes, he insisted on it. He said they did the best curry on the island.'

The doctor snorted impatiently. 'A hot curry, the heat, driving along dangerous roads; it is no wonder he had a heart attack!'

'A heart attack?' Cordelia stared up at him in growing horror. 'Is he—is he . . .?'

'No, he's going to be all right,' Marcus Stone put in quickly before the doctor could answer. 'Evidently the attack was only a minor one, but he suffered some other injuries in the crash; he has severe concussion and has hurt his ankle.'

The doctor, rather put out at being forestalled, added in a severe voice, 'He will get well, slowly, if he keeps calm and does not get excited. But it will be several weeks before he will be well enough to travel back to England. And he is too ill to be moved to a hospital at the moment. He will have to stay here.'

Without hesitation, Marcus Stone said, 'That's no problem. We have plenty of room. Where are you staying?' he asked, turning to Cordelia.

'At the Ladyhill Hotel in Kandy, but . . .'

'Then I'll send someone to explain to them and pick up your things.'

'Oh, but we . . .'

'No buts,' he interrupted. 'You're staying here.'

'Good,' the doctor approved. 'I will send a nurse to sit with him tonight and I will call again tomorrow.'

'Oh, that won't be necessary. I can sit with him,' Cordelia told him.

'You are a nurse?'

'Well, no, but . . .'

'It is better to have a nurse.'

'Can I see him now?'

'I have given him something to make him sleep. You can see him when he wakes up. Now,' the doctor got up, 'I will look at you. Mr Stone tells me you, too, were hurt.'

'It's nothing. Just a few bruises.'

'But better I make sure. You have another room?' he asked, looking at Marcus Stone.

'Yes, of course.'

Seeing that she was outnumbered, Cordelia got to her feet, but her leg had stiffened while she was sitting down and she stumbled and gave an involuntary cry of pain as she went to put her weight on it. In one quick stride Marcus Stone was by her side, his arm supporting her.

'Ouch!' she gasped, clinging to his arm. She had to take a couple of deep breaths and then looked up at him and gave a shaky laugh. 'I seem to be making rather a habit of collapsing on to you. I'm sorry—but I'm very glad you're here,' she told him with sincere gratitude.

Looking up at him, she managed a smile through the pain and expected her rescuer to smile back at her, but his dark, straight brows flickered into a slight frown and a closed look came into his eyes. But then she was being helped into a pleasantly furnished bedroom with double doors leading on to a verandah overlooking the gardens at the side of the bungalow. There were two single beds with woven bedspreads. Marcus Stone helped her to the nearest, then turned and left, holding the door open for the nurse to come in as he did so.

The doctor confirmed that there was nothing seriously wrong, told her not to overdo things for a few days and gave her some pills for her headache. He told her to lie still and rest for a while, but Cordelia couldn't; the first stunned shock of the accident had worn off and she began to realise just how much trouble they were being to their rescuer. She could faintly hear the doctor talking to him now, the little doctor's voice high and foreign, Marcus Stone's deep and so reassuringly British. Marcus Stone—Cordelia was sure she'd heard that name before somewhere, but when she tried to think it made her headache worse. She was worried about her father and at the same time angry with him for not having told her he had a heart condition. If she'd known she could have been more forceful, have insisted that they hire a driver with the car. But it was too late now, the worst had already happened.

The voices in the corridor faded, she heard a car start up outside and drive away, and, five minutes later, it was followed by a second car. Cordelia moved restlessly on the pillow, worrying about what would happen to the car they'd hired, whether it was badly damaged. She sat up on the bed, realising that she should have made some arrangements for taking it to a garage, that she hadn't let the car hire firm know. Picking up her dress, she slipped it back on, then padded out on bare feet into the sitting-room.

Their host was standing by the window, looking out across the garden to the rising hills. He had a lighted cigarette between his fingers, but he wasn't smoking it, it had a long head of ash. He was very still, as if he was completely absorbed in something. Cordelia moved across to him, her bare feet quite silent on the tiled floor. She had thought that he had been intently watching some object outside, but when she came closer she saw that he was mentally absorbed, concentrating on something within himself.

For a while he didn't realise that she was there and she had the opportunity to really look at him, her mind unclouded now by fear for her father. His face in profile was strong and clean-cut with straight nose and high cheekbones. Perhaps a little too thin, the jaw a little too square to be called handsome, and, in repose, there were small lines at the corners of his mouth that gave it a bitter look. His hair was dark and thick, very clean and worn rather longer than was fashionable. His eyelashes, too, were thick and soft, but they were the only hint of softness about the face of Marcus Stone. But despite this, or perhaps because of it, Cordelia felt her senses quicken, his male magnetism attracting her and making her sharply conscious of her own femininity.

When, a few minutes later, he became aware of her presence, he didn't jump or anything, his eyes widened for a second and then he frowned and looked away, saw the ash on his cigarette and crushed it out in an ashtray with what looked to

Cordelia like unnecessary force. 'Can I get you something?' he asked abruptly.

'Well, no, but . . . I'm sorry to bother you, Mr Stone, but I haven't done anything about that car we hired. I ought to let the owners know what's happened. And it will have to be moved . . .'

'That's already been taken care of.' His eyes ran over her, apparently casual, but taking in every detail: her shoulder-length fair hair, her tall slimness, settled for a moment on her bare feet, then travelled up to her face to note her even features and the pallor from a long English winter spent inside an office, the hesitancy in her blue eyes. His own expression softened a little. 'I assure you there's nothing you have to see to or worry about. Everything's under control. I've sent a car to your hotel to explain what's happened and to collect your luggage. It should be back early this evening.'

'But the bill will need paying and . . .'

He moved closer to her, caught hold of her agitated hands. 'Cordelia,' he said firmly, 'I've already told you to stop worrying. Now please go and rest; I'll see that you're called an hour before dinner, or immediately if your father wakes and asks for you.' His hands tightened for a brief second. 'Relax. There really isn't anything for you to do or to worry about.'

And in that moment Cordelia did stop worrying; it was as if she recognised and acknowledged his ability to take control, to efficiently organise and take care of himself and those under his protection. Perhaps it was the strength she felt in his hands, perhaps only her own present vulnerability and weakness, but her anxiety disappeared and she just felt terribly tired. She nodded and he let go her hands.

'Thank you for taking us in. And—and for everything you've done.' Her voice trembled. 'If you hadn't come along . . .'

'Nonsense,' Marcus's tone was brisk. 'It's the least I could do for a couple of compatriots.'

He offered to help her back to her room, but when Cordelia said that she could manage he didn't press it, just stood and watched her as she hobbled along.

She must have slept for a long time, because the sun was setting when she was wakened by a knock on the door and a voice she didn't recognise telling her that dinner would be in one hour. Her two suitcases stood neatly just inside the door and she wondered who at the hotel had repacked them for her. There was a bathroom opening off her room—and the water was hot! Cordelia lowered her stiff, bruised body into it and groaned softly. But it was a blissful kind of agony. She soaked for a good half hour and carefully towelled herself dry, afterwards examining herself in the full-length mirror on the door. Lord, she was going to have one hell of a bruise! Her left side, from her hip right down her thigh, was discoloured. She prodded it gingerly and found that it was also very tender. There were a few marks, too, on her left arm, but those she could hardly feel. She pouted into the mirror; it would look terrible with a bikini and some of it would probably show even under a one-piece.

Cordelia dressed carefully, wishing that she had more clothes with her, but at least she had brought one or two new outfits. She chose a soft, full white top with long sleeves which would hide the marks on her arms, and which had a matching flared skirt. She added white high-heeled sandals which accentuated the slimness of her ankles, and spent some time brushing her hair and doing her make-up. By the time she had finished the hour was almost gone, and she quickly picked up her bag and hurried into the sitting-room with only the slightest limp.

Marcus was pouring himself a drink, but he turned when he heard her heels on the tiled floor. He saw her and seemed to do a double-take, his eyebrows rising in surprise.

'Good evening. I hope I haven't kept you waiting.' Cordelia smiled up at him.

'Not at all. What would you like to drink?' He didn't smile back, after the first look of surprise his face had become quite expressionless.

'Do you have Bacardi and Coke?'

'Of course.'

He turned to pour the drink from a well-stocked cabinet, and she asked, 'Is my father still asleep?'

'I believe so.' Marcus handed her her glass. 'He did wake for a while earlier on, enough to be told that he was all right, and then he went to sleep again.'

'He didn't ask for me?'

Marcus shook his head. 'I expect he was still feeling woozy from the drug the doctor gave him.'

'Yes, I expect so.' Cordelia looked down at her drink, accepting this sop to her pride, then she abruptly changed her mind. Lifting her chin, she said sharply, 'You don't really have to try to protect my feelings, you know. I'm quite old enough to face the fact that he didn't ask for me. I don't suppose he even bothered to ask if I'd been hurt in the crash.'

Marcus looked at her, his eyes for a moment fully alert, concentrating on her face. 'Just how old is old enough?'

Frowning slightly, Cordelia replied, 'I'm twenty.'

'That's young to be so cynical.'

'I'm not being cynical, just realistic.' But even so she couldn't keep a slight trace of bitterness out of her voice.

'When I first saw you I thought you were younger, but now you look so . . .'

'Yes?' Cordelia queried when he hesitated.

'So different,' he finished.

But somehow she had a strange feeling that that wasn't what he'd been going to say at all.

A servant came with quiet feet and voice to say that dinner was ready, and Marcus led her into a smaller room opening off to the right of the sitting-room. This room, too, had its windows open to the cool of the night air so that the flame of the candles on the table flickered a little and cast shadows on the walls. Cordelia took her place opposite him at a round table that was just too large to be intimate, too small to be impersonal.

He made a few small-talk remarks while they were eating their soup and Cordelia guessed that he was being tactful; most people would have followed up her remark about her father and wanted to know why she was so sure he hadn't asked after her. She was already regretting her outburst and so was grateful for his tact, and she tried to keep up her end of the conversation by asking him if he had always lived in Sri Lanka.

'No, but I've been here for nearly two years now.'

'And is this your house? Are you settled here?'

Shaking his head, Marcus answered, 'No, I rent the house from a friend. He had to go and work in America for a couple of years but didn't want to give up this place. I wanted somewhere quiet to work on my—on a project I've undertaken, so it was an ideal arrangement.'

'So your friend will be coming home soon?' Cordelia remarked, wondering what kind of project needed two years to finish but too unsure of herself to ask.

'Within the next few months, I expect, but there's no hard and fast date. We're neither of us tied by time.'

'How marvellous,' Cordelia said wistfully, 'not to be governed by the clock all the time. Not to have to work from nine till five all the year except for three weeks' holiday in the summer and a week at Christmas. Just to go away for a couple of years, give or take a few months.'

An amused glint came into Marcus's blue-grey eyes. 'It isn't quite as simple as that.'

'Isn't it?'

But he didn't follow up the invitation, merely said, 'I take it you work in an office?'

'Yes, for a solicitor.'

'As a secretary?'

'Yes.'

'And you hate it?'

'No, not really.' She tilted her head as she considered the matter, making her hair fall forward against her chin. Absently she put up a hand to lift it away, the gold tendrils curling around her fingers. 'Or at least I didn't while I was there, but now I'm beginning to hate the thought of having to go back.' She laughed slightly. 'My first taste of travel has gone to my head, I suppose.'

He nodded. 'It happens. That's why thousands of young people are always working or travelling abroad. It's a kind of wanderlust that comes with young adulthood and has to be appeased before one can settle down.'

'Is that what you're doing?'

Marcus gave a short laugh. 'Hardly. I got that out of my system quite some time ago. No, I just came here to get away from——' he hesitated and changed what he was going to say, 'because the climate is so good in Sri Lanka and because I wanted peace and quiet in which to work.'

'And now we've come along to interrupt you,' Cordelia said with embarrassment in her voice. 'I'm sorry.'

'Nonsense,' Marcus denied brusquely. 'I'm glad that I was in a position to be able to help, and you're certainly not intruding. Please don't think that. You're welcome to stay until your father feels fit enough to travel. And there are plenty of servants to look after him.'

'But your work?' Cordelia asked uncertainly.

'As a matter of fact it's almost finished. Please don't worry about it.'

He said it in such a final tone that Cordelia took him at his word, sensing that he regretted having mentioned his desire for solitude. He immediately changed the topic of conversation by asking her what she thought of Sri Lanka.

'Well, I think it's wonderful, of course, but then I'm biased because I was born here.' His eyebrow lifted in surprise and she went on to tell him about the circumstances.

'So this was to be a nostalgia trip for your father?'

'Yes, I suppose so,' Cordelia agreed doubtfully. 'Although I've never really thought of him as the type who would go in for that sort of thing.' Not that she really knew with any certainty what type of person he was at all.

After dinner she went quietly into her father's room to watch him while the nurse had a meal. She sat in a chair by the side of his bed and looked at him, studied him more closely than she had ever done before. But there was little to tell from his hard profile, from the lines in his leathery face that came from too many years spent in the sun. Cordelia realised that she really knew very little about her father and only had the biased idea of his character that she had picked up over the years from her mother and her aunt, and which was naturally prejudiced against him. Not that anything had ever been said directly against him; it was more an opinion formed from overheard conversations, from remarks that had been cut off in mid-sentence when it was realised that she was in the vicinity. And, added to that, was his boorish behaviour of the last two days which had done nothing to make her alter her opinion, had even emphasised it.

As she watched him, James Allingham's eyelids flickered and he moved his head on the pillow. His eyes opened and Cordelia stood up and moved a little closer. For a few moments his eyes travelled bemusedly round the strange, dimly-lit room, then he became aware of someone with him. A flash of joy came into his face, eagerly he spoke a word she didn't understand, perhaps it was a name. Quickly she moved forward to the edge of the bed, leaned over him so that she was within the light. The joy died from his face and he said heavily, 'Oh, it's you.'

Somehow Cordelia stopped herself from turning on her heel and walking out of the room. Tight-lipped, she managed to say, 'Yes, it's me. How do you feel?'

He snorted. 'Bloody awful! What—what happened?' He tried to move painfully in the bed. 'I—I can't seem to remember.'

'There was an accident,' Cordelia told him, coldly, unemotionally. 'The car went off the road.' But she didn't tell him about the heart attack; it was up to the doctor to tell him that if he thought his patient well enough to know.

'Where are we? At a hotel?'

'No. We've been taken in by an Englishman. This house is near where we crashed. The man's name is Marcus Stone. He . . .'

But already her father's eyes were closing again, as if the effort of concentrating for even those few minutes had been too much for him. Cordelia's voice faded and she stood staring down at him, wondering just who he had thought was with him, what had brought such joy for an instant to his face. The name he'd said hadn't been that of anyone she knew; it certainly hadn't been her mother's.

The nurse came back soon after and, in a whispered conversation, Cordelia told her that her patient had wakened. The nurse nodded, obviously perfectly capable of dealing with the invalid. She was quite young and much smaller than Cordelia, but then the Sri Lankans were a race of short people, not many of them came up to her height, but the nurse seemed to take caring for someone who was so much bigger than herself all in her stride.

Cordelia went back to the sitting-room. Marcus wasn't there, but from behind a closed door to the left she could hear the sound of a typewriter and guessed that he was catching up on his work, so she decided not to disturb him by going in to say goodnight. The room was still open to the night, the wooden shutters not yet closed, and she wandered out on to the verandah that ran all round the house. The scents of the flowers filled the air and she put up a hand to touch the delicate trumpets of the mauve and white bougainvillea that grew up the supports and along the roof like a rich and colourful vine. There were some steps leading down to the garden and Cordelia went slowly down them, the moon lighting her way. The garden was quite large by English standards and was walled all round, but it was planted with trees that gave off the exotic, spicy smells of nutmeg and sandalwood, and with flowering bushes of hibiscus and frangipani.

Somehow the night seemed to heighten the scents and Cordelia followed her nose, moving from one bush to another, recognising cinnamon, cloves and, from way back in her childhood, the camphor that reminded her of best clothes packed away with mothballs to protect them.

Her slow progress through the garden had brought her opposite the room in which Marcus was working, and a movement from inside made her look up. The windows in the room were closed, but there were no curtains. He had got up to get a book from a shelf and now sat down again at the typewriter. It was very much a working room, the walls lined with shelves, mostly full of books, and there were a couple of steel filing cabinets under a big map that had been pinned to the wall. He started typing again and Cordelia smiled to herself; he was very much a pick-and-peck typist, was probably only using two fingers.

Her own speeds were very fast and she was proud of them, but then her smile faded as she remembered that they were now more or less obsolete and she had had to train all over again on a word processor.

Idly she wondered what work Marcus did; she tried to see what the map on the wall was of, but it was too far away. It didn't look like Sri Lanka.

His desk was sideways on to the window, the light shining fully on him. He seemed to be typing from a sheaf of notes, pausing every now and again to think or to make an alteration. Once or twice he made a mistake in the typing and she could see and hear his annoyance as he impatiently x'ed out the error and retyped it. He paused to think again, got up and selected a book from one of the shelves, moved towards the window as he turned the pages. Cordelia watched him, feeling safe under her cover of darkness. He seemed too big for the room; he really needed one that he could pace up and down in while he sorted out his thoughts, but his long legs would only be able to take a few steps in the confines of that study.

As she watched him, still intent on the book in his hands, it came to Cordelia that he was a very attractive man—attractive to women, that was. There was something powerful and slightly arrogant about the set of his shoulders, the thrust of his chin. The sort of man who could handle and take charge of whatever came his way—much as he had taken charge of her and her father that very day. And she rather thought that he was quite capable of handling women, too. She shivered a little, but not from cold, and moved nearer the window, her dress mottled in the moonlight by the branches of a jasmine bush. There was something about Marcus Stone that she had never met in any other man before and which she found difficult to define; magnetism perhaps, or just a super-abundance of pure basic masculinity? Not the flashy, flauntingly virile kind, but controlled power, machismo kept well in hand.

Without warning, Marcus thrust the window open and stepped out on to the verandah. 'Who's there?' he demanded sharply.

'Cordelia.' She moved forward into the light as she identified herself. 'I was just taking a stroll round the garden.'

'I hope you sprayed yourself with insect repellent first, or you'll be covered in mosquito bites,' he remarked drily.

'Yes, I did.' Climbing the steps to the verandah, she said on a note of apology, 'Please don't let me keep you from your work.'

'It's all right; typing is the part I enjoy least.' He reached in his pocket for a cigarette and lit it. 'How was your father?'

'He woke up. I just told him that there'd been an accident; I thought it better not to tell him about his heart attack. What do you think?'

'You're probably right. Talk to Dr Matara about it in the morning.'

Cordelia was leaning against the upright supporting the verandah and he moved to her side, leaning down to balance his elbows on the rail.

'How long were you intending to stay in Sri Lanka?' he asked.

'There was no fixed time limit; my father wanted to stay here for several weeks.'

'Good, then you won't have any worries about rushing back to England.'

'No.'

They both fell silent, not the kind of silence in which one tries desperately to think of something to say, but a tacit, companionable silence in which they listened to the soft sounds of the night that broke the quiet stillness: the splashing of a nearby waterfall, the jarring cry of a nightbird diving on its prey. Marcus drew on his cigarette, the glow highlighting the hard clean lines of his face. His shoulder touched her arm and she gave an involuntary shiver.

Marcus straightened up. 'You're cold.'

'A—a little.' Cordelia's throat felt strangely tight so that she stammered over the words.

'Come inside. Perhaps the shock of the accident hasn't completely worn off yet.'

He steered her through the door into his study and Cordelia headed for the inner door, glancing round with interest as she passed through the room. 'I am feeling rather tired, despite the rest I had earlier on . . .' Her voice trailed away as she frowned at the map on the wall; it seemed to be of some inland area with foreign-sounding names, and there was a long, irregular line drawn along most of its length. Her eyes travelled over the titles of some of the books on the shelves that covered the left hand wall. Reaching the door, she started to say 'Goodnight,' stopped, and then turned to stare at him 'You're Marcus Stone!'

The grey-blue eyes looked amused. 'I know,' he agreed gravely.

'But—I mean—you're *the* Marcus Stone. The writer. You wrote that fantastic book about the Great Wall of China.'

'I'm glad you enjoyed it.'

'Oh, I *did*.' Cordelia's hand left the door knob and she stepped back into the room, her eyes sparkling with excitement and interest. 'You made it seem so alive. You made me long to go there and see it for myself.'

The amused look faded as he gave a quick smile of real pleasure. 'Thank you; you couldn't have said anything about it that I would have appreciated more.'

Cordelia grew suddenly shy. 'I'm sure you must have heard it a million times already.'

He laughed. 'Oh, not a million, I assure you.'

'I've read a couple of your other books,' she told him. 'I'd like to read them all, but there are always such long waiting lists for them at the library.'

'Perhaps you'd like to borrow one now,' he offered, the laughter still in his voice. 'I have copies of most of them here.'

'Thank you.' Cordelia selected a book and turned to him. 'Are you—are you working on a book about Sri Lanka?'

'No. This one's about another wall—the Berlin Wall.'

'I guess one wall led to another?' she quipped, her confidence coming back.

'Something like that.' His face changed, became withdrawn and introspective. 'Humanity has been building walls to keep people out since the beginning of civilisation.'

'Or to keep people in,' Cordelia added quietly.

His eyes flicked over her. 'As you say. There are too many walls, too many barriers.'

And yet, despite his protest, he had just built a small one himself, between the two of them, Cordelia thought. She softly said goodnight again, but Marcus didn't answer, merely nodded abstractedly, his gaze fixed on the map with its thick red wall like a line of blood, and she knew that his thoughts were whole continents away.

CHAPTER THREE

CORDELIA undressed quickly and got into bed, intending to read for half an hour, but even though she was looking forward to reading the book, she found that she just couldn't concentrate. She had never met a writer before, or anyone who was in the least famous, if it came to that, and the thought excited her. She wished now that she had asked him lots more questions, found out more about his work, but perhaps she could ask him another time; there should be lots of opportunities while she was staying in the same house. That was if he was willing to talk about it; although other people obviously found it intensely interesting, perhaps to writers it was just their job and they got bored when people asked them questions about it all the time.

Giving up any attempt to read, Cordelia closed the book and hugged it to her, too excited to go to sleep. The last two or three Marcus Stone books had all been best-sellers, and she had little doubt that the one on the Berlin Wall would be no exception. How marvellous to know about the book before it had even been published! Perhaps Marcus might even let her read the manuscript, she hoped dreamily, ambitiously. And perhaps he might not; her thoughts grew more prosaic, more down-to-earth. As an uninvited guest in his house it was really up to her to be as unobtrusive as possible, to keep out of his way so that he could get on with his work in uninterrupted solitude.

Cordelia didn't know much about how writers worked, but she imagined that they spent long hours alone with the phone off the hook and a 'do not disturb' sign on the door. But then she remembered that Marcus had said that the book was almost finished—and also that he disliked typing. Maybe there was a way in which she could get to read the manuscript, and perhaps at the same time repay their host in some small measure for his kindness. If she offered to type for him ... Her eyes sparkled and she gripped the book more tightly. She imagined herself sharing his workroom with him, seated at a smaller desk, typing, while he worked on something else. Perhaps she would ask him a question and he would come over, lean close to her as he explained. Perhaps his shoulder would touch her arm again as it had done tonight. Cordelia put down the book and turning off the light, lay in bed feeling hot and strangely aware of her whole body. It was as if every nerve end, every pore of her skin, was waiting and expectant. It felt like that for quite some time until at last she fell asleep.

The idea of offering to type for Marcus was so strong in her mind that it was the first thing she thought of when she woke the next morning. She showered and dressed quickly, putting on one of the new dresses that she had bought specially for this holiday, and adding careful make-up. A table had been laid for breakfast out on the verandah where there was a breathtaking view looking out over the green hills of the tea plantations. But this morning Cordelia had little attention to spare for the view. Marcus wasn't there, so she turned to the white-jacketed servant who pulled out a chair for her and asked him where his employer was.

'Mr Stone has gone out, madam.'

'Oh. Will he be gone long?' The disappointment was clear in her voice.

'I think he will be back soon. Please—how do you want your eggs?'

Cordelia chose scrambled. Happier now that she knew Marcus hadn't gone out for the whole day, she took in the view, noticing the small, bright patches of colour among the tea bushes where groups of women worked slowly along the rows, picking the tea leaves and putting them into the large baskets tied on their backs. She saw a lorry travelling along a road and wondered if it was the same road that she and father had used yesterday, but decided that it was too near, that it must only be a secondary road leading up to a tea factory. After she had eaten her breakfast, she amused herself by reading the local English language newspaper that the houseboy brought her while she drank another cup of coffee, but presently a movement among the bushes in the garden caught her eye and she saw Marcus walking up a path between the trees. Her heart gave a crazy kind of jerk of excitement and she sat forward eagerly, but then grew suddenly still. He wasn't alone. There was a girl with him—a petite, graceful native girl with large, dark eyes set in a clear dusky skin. As they came nearer Cordelia saw that the girl was beautiful. She also saw that she, too, was being scrutinised just as closely and that there was an openly hostile look on the other girl's face.

But then the look was gone as the girl lowered her eyes and demurely followed Marcus up the steps to the verandah.

'Good morning. How are you feeling today?'

'Fine, thank you.' Cordelia gave him a rather

forced smile, intensely curious about the silent girl
beside him, but trying not to let it show.

'No ill effects from the accident?'

She shook her head. 'No, none.'

'Good. How's your father? Have you been in to
see him yet?'

'No. I thought I'd leave it until after the doctor
came. Aren't you going to join me?' she added
when he made no move to sit down.

'I've already eaten.' The Sri Lankan girl was
standing a little behind him, but now he put out a
hand and drew her forward. 'By the way, this is
Sugin. If you need anything just ask her and she'll
take care of it for you.'

The girl he called Sugin put her hands together
and bowed in the traditional, respectful manner.
'*Ayou bowan.*'

'*Ayou bowan,*' Cordelia returned the greeting,
and felt a small flash of satisfaction as the native
girl's eyes flickered in surprise at her correct
pronunciation.

Marcus said, 'If you'll excuse me, I have an
appointment.'

He took his hand from where it had been resting
casually and familiarly on the other girl's arm and
moved to go in, but stopped when Cordelia
exclaimed, 'Oh, but I wanted to speak to you. To
ask you something.'

'Yes?' His left eyebrow rose enquiringly.

She hesitated, looking from him to Sugin
uncertainly. 'I—er—perhaps I could see you when
you get back?'

'Okay. I'll only be gone for an hour or so. Sugin
will look after you.'

He raised his hand in a half salute of farewell
and stepped briskly inside, leaving the two alone

together. Sugin made no effort to speak, so Cordelia forced herself to say stiffly, 'I take it you work for Mr Stone?'

The native girl's eyelids flickered and she hesitated for a fraction of a second before saying, in a tone that Cordelia thought had a note of mockery in it, 'Yes, miss.'

'Well, there's nothing I want right now, thank you. You'd better—get on with your work.' She had almost said 'go about your duties' but thought how dated that sounded, then realised it must be a throwback from when she had lived in Sri Lanka before; in her mind she could still hear her mother's gentle but firm voice instructing the servants that they had employed all those years ago.

Sugin turned and walked away, making no attempt to give a respectful bow now that Marcus wasn't there.

Cordelia looked blindly down at the newspaper as she wondered about the girl's position in Marcus's household—in Marcus's life! Dimly she remembered having seen a girl waiting at the door when she had first arrived here, but she had been so shaken up at the time that she hadn't really taken much notice, could only recall the girl having been sent hurrying off to make up a bed for her father, but not having seen her after that.

Looking down the garden, Cordelia couldn't help thinking that it seemed rather odd for Sugin and Marcus to have come from that direction. It was possible, she supposed, for them to have been inspecting the garden or perhaps just taking a stroll while they talked over household concerns, but in that case they must have taken a long time about it, because she hadn't seen them go out.

Folding the paper, she gave a quick look round to make sure Sugin wasn't watching her, then got to her feet and went down the verandah steps into the garden, retracing the path that they had taken.

The garden was just as delightful to the eye during the daytime as it had been to her sense of smell last night, but Cordelia for once paid little heed to the beauty around her, walking quickly across the grass that grew between the bushes and trees until she came to the wall that surrounded the garden. It was quite a high wall with broken glass embedded in the top, whether to keep out animal or human predators Cordelia couldn't tell. The path curved round a tangled mass of bougainvillea bushes just near the wall, and behind them was a solid gate set into its thickness, with a key in the lock.

Cordelia tried to open the gate by pulling at the handle, but whoever had come through it last had locked it behind them. She turned the key and the gate opened easily and silently, its hinges well oiled. Beyond the gate the path continued through a field where a few tethered goats cropped at the sparse growth of grass, then through another, much smaller gate, in a low stone wall, into a track that ran in front of a few spaced-out native houses where barefooted children played in the dust. She didn't go out there, just stood looking for a while, taking it all in, then closed the gate and locked it again and slowly walked back through the garden. Probably it was a short cut for any of Marcus's servants who lived in the houses; it must save them a long walk if they could avoid going round by the road. Perhaps Marcus had been visiting someone in the houses and Sugin had walked back with him. Perhaps he had ... Oh, it could be anything!

Cordelia shook her head, angry with herself. She was just pulling ideas out of thin air. Anything rather than contemplate the more obvious conclusion. And after all, what was it to her if Marcus came *to* the house early in the morning with a young girl and admitted that he'd breakfasted elsewhere? After all, the man had been living here alone for nearly two years; it was hardly surprising if he'd formed a relationship of some sort, with someone. It was really none of her business and she wouldn't think about it again, Cordelia told herself determinedly, then thought about nothing else all morning.

A servant came to find her, telling her that Dr Matara had arrived. After examining her father again, he came to tell her that he was in a weak condition and it might be several weeks before he would be fit enough to make the long journey back to England.

'How long will it be before he'll be well enough to move to a hotel?' Cordelia asked, not quite sure now what answer she wanted to hear.

The doctor pursed his lips. 'It is difficult to say. Two weeks at least. I would prefer three to be on the safe side. The nearest hotels are at Nuwara Eliya, which will be better for him as it is not so hot as on the coast. But are you in a hurry to leave here? I thought it was already arranged with Mr Stone.'

'What was arranged with Mr Stone?' Marcus had returned without them hearing him and picked up the end of their conversation.

The doctor immediately detailed what had gone before and Marcus gave her a speculative look. 'Of course Mr Allingham can stay until he's well enough. Unless . . .' he turned towards her. 'Have you spoken to your father this morning?'

'No.' Cordelia shook her head.

'I see.' He held out his hand to Dr Matara. 'Thanks for cóming. Shall we see you tomorrow?' The two men shook hands and Marcus shepherded him out. When he came back he paused for a minute, then said, 'I'm sorry if you find it boring here.'

'It isn't that,' Cordelia assured him uncomfortably. 'Of course I'm not bored. It's just that—well, I feel that we ought not to impose on your hospitality—your kindness.' She paused uncertainly. 'After all, we're complete strangers. We have no right to . . .'

'But we're all British and a long way from home,' Marcus interposed. 'Don't you think that gives you some claim?'

'No, not really,' Cordelia said honestly. 'At least, it shouldn't. My father should never have come here knowing that he had a weak heart.'

Marcus moved across the room and sat down in an easy chair. 'Maybe he had some definite reason for coming back. Something that had to be done despite his illness—or because of it.'

'What do you mean?' Cordelia sat in a chair nearby.

Marcus shrugged. 'Men often feel after an illness that they ought to put their affairs in order in case it happens again. Or they feel that they have to fulfil a lifetime dream before it's too late.' He paused to light a cigarette while Cordelia digested this, then added, 'Didn't he give you any reason for wanting to come back here?'

'He just said he wanted to see the island again and to convalesce after his illness.'

'That was all?'

'Yes.'

'Strange.' He blew out smoke and the air-conditioning drew it upwards in a twisting spiral. 'Was that what you wanted to talk to me about?'

'Oh. No.' His eyebrows rose enquiringly, but she hesitated before answering, all the confidence and sense of excited anticipation that had filled her last night lost in uncertainty now. 'It was just that—last night I heard you trying to type and . . .'

His left eyebrow rose steeply above the other. '*Trying* to type?'

'Well, yes. A trained typist can always tell when someone picks out one letter at a time.'

Marcus grinned. 'You're quite right; I'm no typist. Sorry, I interrupted you. What were you going to say?'

'I just wondered if, while I was here, I might help you by doing some typing for you. My speeds are quite good and I make very few mistakes.'

Her voice fell away as she surprised a sudden alert look on Marcus's face. Then he said abruptly, 'It's very kind of you, but you're here on holiday and have hardly seen anything of the place yet. You must take the car and get out and about, see all the tourist sites.'

Cordelia hesitated, rather taken aback. 'But I should *like* to work for you.'

'Why?' Again that penetrating look.

'Because . . .' She groped for reasons. 'Because I should like, in some small measure, to repay you for your kindness and . . .'

'I don't want any repayment,' he cut in shortly.

Her head came up. 'Well, want it or not, I should still like to do it,' she retorted in a tone of determined sharpness, and saw a gleam of amusement come into his eyes.

'And the other reason you were about to give me?' he demanded.

'What? Oh, well . . .' She flushed a little, then said on a wistful, almost confiding note, 'I would like to act as secretary for a real writer. To feel that I've had even such a small part in the production of a book.'

He smiled. 'Are you a book person, Cordelia?'

'Oh, yes! I can read anywhere.'

'Even in the bath?'

She laughed. 'Especially in the bath.'

He laughed in return and Cordelia's heart felt a surge of excitement again, all her doubts forgotten, and she knew an instant of pure happiness.

'All right, you've got yourself a job. I did have a woman who came in to type, but her husband was taken ill with malaria and she has to stay home and look after him, so I'll be more than glad to give up my two-fingered attempts. But you must still see something of the island,' he added firmly. 'This must be a holiday as well. Now,' he stood up, 'I expect you'd like to go and visit your father.'

'When shall I start work?' she asked enthusiastically.

Marcus laughed again and put a restraining hand on her arm as she got to her feet. 'Don't be so eager! You might find me a slavedriver.'

'Oh, I'm sure you wouldn't be,' she answered easily, and then felt her throat go suddenly dry as she wondered what it would be like if she was really his slave. 'Would you?' she added softly, raggedly.

But he had let go her arm and turned away, hadn't heard or noticed anything, fortunately. He held the door open for her and then went to his study while she crossed to her father's room and knocked on the door. The nurse gave her a smiling welcome, but James Allingham, who was sitting up in bed, propped up by pillows, had only a short nod for her.

'Good morning, Father.' She made no attempt to kiss him and even the title Father came uneasily to her tongue. 'You look much better today.' This got no answer, so she tried again. 'Is there anything I can get you? Or do for you? Perhaps you'd like me to read to you for a while?'

'There's nothing wrong with my eyes,' he told her harshly. 'If I wanted to read I'm quite capable of doing so.'

'Yes, of course,' Cordelia agreed coldly. She waited a moment, then said, 'There's nothing you want, then?'

He frowned. 'Our things we left at the hotel in Kandy; I gather they've been brought here?'

'Yes.'

'Did you go and fetch them?'

'No. Mr Stone sent his driver for them. Someone at the hotel must have packed them into the cases. Why, is something missing?'

Ignoring the question, he said, 'Did you unpack my case?'

'No. I unpacked my own. I'm not sure who unpacked your things—I think it was the head houseboy. Why?' she asked again.

Some tension seemed to go out of him and James Allingham relaxed against the pillows. 'It's no matter. Just wondered, that's all.'

Cordelia looked down at her father, trying to guess just what it was he had in his luggage that he didn't want her to see. A sharp rap sounded at the door and as she was nearest she opened it.

Marcus said, 'I wonder if your father is feeling well enough for me to meet him yet?'

'Yes, of course.'

She stood back to let him in, then shut the door and introduced the two men. They seemed to size each other up while she was speaking, then James Allingham shook Marcus's hand in a grip that was still firm despite his weakness.

Marcus didn't stay long; he merely assured the invalid that he was welcome at the bungalow as long as he needed to stay, and that he had only to ask for anything he wanted. 'And when you're feeling better we must have a chat about what Sri Lanka was like in the old days,' Marcus added easily. 'Cordelia told me that you used to manage one of the tea plantations and that she was born here. It's a great shame that you won't be fit enough to take her round the island yourself, as you intended, but I'll try to make sure she sees something of the place.'

Her father gave an abstracted nod, obviously not caring what Cordelia saw or didn't see, which made Marcus frown, but then he seemed to pull himself together a little and said, 'It's really most kind of you. But you mustn't let Cordelia be a nuisance. She can quite easily go and stay at a hotel or a rest-house somewhere until I'm fit again, you know.'

Cordelia's face paled at his rudeness. Stiffly, she said to Marcus, 'Would you excuse me?' then turned and marched out of the room.

Marcus must have left almost immediately after, because he soon followed her out into the garden where she had gone to try and walk off her anger. He gave her a deceptively casual look, his writer's eyes taking everything in, noting her anger and the bewilderment behind it.

Falling into step beside her, he said, 'I know it's none of my business, but if it would help to talk about it . . .'

Cordelia would have loved to talk about it if she had known what to say. But how to explain her father's overt dislike, a relationship based on nothing more solid than a blood tie, a journey undertaken together for selfish reasons on both sides, a reason on her father's side that she didn't even know and was beginning to be afraid of. None of it made for pleasant hearing. Slowly she shook her head. 'It's nothing. Really.'

'Nothing? When your father makes it obvious he doesn't want your company and talks about you as if you weren't there?'

A bright flush of colour heightened her cheeks and she looked at him with dark, unhappy eyes. 'Please,' she said entreatingly.

Marcus continued to look at her frowningly for a moment, then abruptly began to tell her about his visit to China when he had been researching his book on the Great Wall. He talked for quite a while as they walked slowly round the garden and the tension gradually left her. Once he reached up to push a low branch of mauve bougainvillea out of the way and paused to break off a sweep of blooms and give it to her. He went on talking easily, not looking at her, giving her time to recover, until he glanced at his watch and then at her face and saw that she was absorbed in his story. 'Lunchtime, I think,' he said firmly. 'I'll tell you the rest while we're eating.'

After lunch he took her into his study and cleared a place for her at a side table. Cordelia was surprised to find that the typewriter was a modern electric one. 'Can you use it?' he asked her.

'Oh, yes. This wasn't the machine you were using last night, though, was it?'

'No, I have a portable I drag around everywhere with me. I get on better with that.' He brought a wad of typed A4 paper over. 'This is what I was working on; it's the third draft of the book. I've been over it and made a whole lot of alterations and amendments and I was retyping it chapter by chapter. But if you could take that over from me, it would be marvellous.'

Cordelia smiled. 'I think I can manage that.'

'Good girl,' he said warmly, so warmly that Cordelia started to glow inside. 'If you have any difficulties or there's anything you don't understand, just sing out.'

'The only problem will probably be that I'll get so interested I'll stop and read it.'

He grinned and went over to his own big desk where there was another pile of typed sheets and began to go slowly through them.

Cordelia tried to work quietly, afraid of disturbing him, but the electric typewriter made little noise and he was obviously used to it, for he wrote on steadily. She felt a great feeling of peace and contentment, working there with the sun pouring through the open windows into the quiet room. The book was absorbing and she had no real difficulty in deciphering his thick, black handwriting, although after a while she cheated and asked him to explain something. He came over at once but didn't bend over her, instead pulling the sheet of paper round at right angles so that he could read it, then explained what he'd meant and what he wanted to convey. Which wasn't quite what she'd hoped for but in no way spoilt the afternoon.

They stopped at about four-thirty and went out on the verandah to have afternoon tea served in delicate china cups, Marcus insisting that she try it the Sri Lankan way without any milk or sugar. 'The Sri Lankans think that the way the English drink tea is a downright crime,' he told her. 'They always drink the pure tea, none of your blended stuff—in fact they consider that to be little better than dust. And they never put in milk or sugar, just use stronger or weaker tea to their liking, although they occasionally indulge in a slice of lemon.'

He passed her a cup and Cordelia sipped experimentally, then pulled a face. 'I think my insides must have got used to the English dust! I don't think I could ever get to like this.'

'Try again,' he encouraged her. 'It grows on you after a while.'

She laughed and bent to obey him, but stopped with the cup halfway to her lips as Sugin came out on to the verandah. Without waiting for an invitation she seated herself at the tea-table. Something flickered at the back of Marcus's eyes, then they were hooded again as he poured tea into a third cup and handed it to the native girl. She sipped delicately and then, as if he had asked a silent question, nodded and said, 'Yes, that is how I like it.'

Marcus turned to Cordelia and said smoothly, 'You must get Sugin to dance for you one evening. The Sri Lankans have their own folk dances and Sugin is very good. She sometimes appears with the Kandyan folk dancers who perform for tourists.'

'How interesting,' Cordelia remarked stiltedly, and asked Sugin how long she had been dancing, while all the time wondering if that was where Marcus had met her. Had he gone like all the tourists to see the dancers and picked Sugin out, brought her back here to be—to be his mistress?

'For many years,' the native girl answered. 'You must start when you are a very young child to learn all the movements, all the dances. The dances are very precise and it takes much skill and gracefulness to become an expert.' The words were said in a polite, almost toneless voice, but were accompanied with a little curl of the lip that clearly told Cordelia that she would be far too gauche and clumsy ever to achieve such perfection.

Setting down her cup, Cordelia stood up and said, 'I'm afraid I'll never get a taste for this. If you'll excuse me, I think I'll go and finish that chapter I was working on.'

'There's no need,' Marcus assured her. 'Tomorrow will do.'

'But I'd like to finish it.' She smiled at him and gave a brief nod to Sugin, then left them alone together. But back in the study she didn't start typing again immediately; instead she absently picked up the spray of bougainvillea that Marcus had picked for her earlier and which she had put into a little pot of water on her desk. She looked at it absently, smoothing her finger over the soft petals, remembering how much she had enjoyed working with him, how right it had felt, and how everything had changed the minute Sugin showed up. Cordelia wasn't used to sophisticated, good-looking men of the world and she realised that she found Marcus exciting and attractive, and that he was famous too only added gilt to the gingerbread. It was a heady kind of excitement, one that she didn't have much idea how to cope with, but the presence of Sugin brought her down to earth with a thud again every time the girl made her quiet but disturbing appearance. Cordelia tried to think rationally, telling herself that Marcus was merely being kind, that he had no interest in her as a woman at all, only as someone who was in trouble and whom he had been able to help. But that, unfortunately, didn't stop her feeling attracted to him. She sighed and sternly told herself off; much better for you, my girl, if you just treat him as your host and temporary boss. Resolutely she began to type, but presently the sound of voices raised in laughter reached her through the open window; Marcus's deep and amused, Sugin's light, but to Cordelia's ears unnecessarily loud, as if the native girl wanted her to hear. Cordelia's flying fingers grew still, paused, then went on more slowly.

A little later she heard a footstep on the verandah and turned her head to see. Marcus stood framed in the window. The sun was setting and his tall, strong body was outlined against the brilliant red and gold of the sky. He put out an arm to lean against the wooden frame and said, 'I won't be in to dinner tonight, Cordelia. The government are building a big dam in the hills and there are a lot of Europeans working on the project. They've formed an Expatriates Club and I usually go up there a couple of times a week. I could ask Sugin to stay with you if you'd rather not be by yourself.'

'No.' Cordelia stood up abruptly.

'All right. Pack up working now. It's getting dark and you'll strain your eyes.'

He moved a few steps into the room, came close to her, but she couldn't see his face very clearly because he stood in front of the glowing sky.

Impulsively she asked, 'Who is Sugin?' and stared up at him, waiting for an answer.

'Sugin?' Marcus gave her one of his quick, searching looks, then said slowly, 'She came with the bungalow.'

So what was she supposed to make of that? Before she could say anything further, he casually put a hand on her shoulder and said, 'I'm putting the car and an English-speaking driver at your disposal tomorrow. Work out tonight where you'd like him to take you. There's the ancient Buddhist city of Anuradhapura, or Sigiriya, which has the most breathtaking views if you're brave enough to climb to the top. I'll leave you out some maps so that you can study them more closely.'

'Thank you.' Hesitatingly she added, 'Will you—be able to come with me?'

His hand was still on her shoulder and she seemed to feel him hesitate for a second, then he removed it and shook his head. 'I'm sorry, but I want to get on with the book tomorrow.'

'Then I'll stay and help you,' Cordelia responded instantly.

Again he shook his head. 'Certainly not! This is supposed to be your holiday. You must go out tomorrow and perhaps help me again the day after.'

His tone was firm, decisive, and Cordelia realised she couldn't argue against it. 'All right. Thank you.'

'Good. I probably won't be back until pretty late tonight, so I'll see you tomorrow. Give my apologies to your father, will you?'

He raised a hand in salute and left Cordelia to

tidy the papers she had been working on, feeling strangely dejected at the thought of a long evening alone, but at least being alone was infinitely better than being with Sugin for several hours.

After eating her solitary meal, she went in to see her father and found him sitting up in bed reading. There was a little more colour in his sallow cheeks and he seemed better, though still as disinclined to have her around. Cordelia wondered rather bitterly why he had bothered to bring her to Sri Lanka at all when it was so obvious that he had no time for her. He would have done better to have paid a nurse to keep him company and look after him.

Going into the lounge, she curled up in an armchair with the book that Marcus had lent her. It was one of his earlier books, a novel, for he wrote both with equal skill, and she was soon completely absorbed, lost to the reality of the world around her, the book holding her so that she was unaware of the passing of time. The houseboy came quietly into the room and set a drink down on the small table beside her, but Cordelia hardly noticed, although her hand went out and she absently sipped the drink. The house grew quiet as the servants went home to bed, but she went on reading, unable to put the book down.

It was almost three in the morning before Marcus came home and, noticing the strip of light under the sitting-room door, went to investigate and found her still sitting in the pool of light thrown by a standard lamp and just a few pages of the book left to read. Cordelia wasn't aware of his arrival, and he had time to reach her side and look at the title of the book before she gave a gasp of fright as she realised that someone was there.

'Oh, it's you! You made me jump.'

'Do you know what the time is?'

'Why?' She glanced at her watch. 'Lord, is it as late as that?'

'You ought to be in bed.'

'I only have this chapter to finish.'

'Leave it till the morning,' he ordered.

'Are you crazy? I wouldn't be able to sleep for wondering what happened at the end. Go away so that I can finish it in peace,' she ordered in her turn, and quite as firmly.

Marcus chuckled, went over to the drinks cabinet and poured liquid from various bottles into a tall glass that he stirred with a long spoon. Then he sat in a chair opposite and watched her silently while Cordelia read on. At last she turned the final page, closed the book and gave a deep sigh of sheer contentment. Again becoming aware of him, Cordelia looked at Marcus with awe in her blue eyes and said almost reverently, 'That was wonderful—one of the best books I've ever read. Oh, *how* I wish I could write like that!'

'Have you ever tried?'

She shook her head. 'I know I couldn't.'

'You don't know what you can do until you try.'

'I know I couldn't do that. How did you start writing?' she asked curiously.

He stood up, setting down his empty glass. 'This is no time to start going into my life story—even if I wanted to,' he remarked drily. Coming across, he put his hands on her arms and pulled her to her feet. 'Go to bed. You'll be . . .' He broke off as she swayed, her legs having gone numb from being tucked under her for so long. 'Careful!' He caught hold of her and held her.

'My legs have gone to sleep.' Cordelia clung to the lapels of the light jacket he was wearing. There was the tang of tobacco and woody aftershave about his clothes. She moved to steady herself and one hand slipped inside his jacket and she could feel his heart beating under her palm. His body felt very hard, very hot. Slowly she raised her eyes and found him looking down at her, his blue-grey eyes glinting in the shadows thrown by the lamp. A queer breathless feeling filled her throat, her chest. She said, 'Marcus?' in an unsteady, strangled tone, and her arms slid up around his neck almost of their own volition. For a moment he continued to gaze down at her, then his arms tightened, pulling her roughly against him, and his lips came down to find hers, fastening on them compulsively, almost like a man who had been hungry for love for a long time. Cordelia's senses reeled, her lips parting before the importunity of his mouth. For a moment she was suspended in delight, enthralled by the warmth of his lips, but then a great surge of desire filled her and she began to return his kiss, her body intimately close to his as she surrendered to his embrace.

She didn't know how long it went on for, but it was much, much too soon when Marcus's lips left hers and he raised his head and loosened his hold. She stayed where she was with her arms around his neck, her lips parted sensuously, her eyes half closed in desire. When he didn't kiss her again she moved against him provocatively, but to her chagrin he only gave a low, amused chuckle and flicked a casual finger against her chin.

'Come on, young lady, it's time for all good little girls to be in bed.'

Cordelia recognised the mocking tone in his

voice and knew that he wouldn't kiss her again, that there had been nothing serious in it, but she decided to tease him a little, so she kept her arms round his neck and said with a sexy pout, 'Is that a proposition, Mr Stone?'

He laughed. 'Minx! Are you going to go to bed or do I have to pick you up and carry you?'

'Mmm, now there's no doubt about it; *that* really was a proposition.'

'Girls who don't obey me,' he told her, 'run the risk of being put across my knee and given a spanking.'

'Wow!' Cordelia's eyes opened very wide. 'Real he-man stuff, huh? This is getting more interesting by the minute!'

His eyes laughed down at hers in genuine amusement. Reaching up, he pulled down her arms and held her a little away from him. 'I wonder what you'd do if I really propositioned you,' he said jokingly, but with just a hint of seriousness in the question.

Cordelia felt her chest tighten again as she remembered his kiss. 'I don't know,' she said thickly. 'Why don't you try it some time?'

His eyes searched her face, but he was teasing again as he said lightly, 'Maybe I will—some time.'

Quickly she looked away, then put a hand up to cover a fake yawn. 'You're right, I am tired. Goodnight, Marcus.'

'Goodnight.'

Crossing to the door, she paused a moment to look back at him. Their eyes met briefly, then Marcus deliberately turned to switch off the lamp.

Cordelia undressed as quietly as she could, afraid of waking her father, whose room was nearby. Slipping into bed, she lay awake, her fair hair spread across the whiteness of the pillow. On any ordinary night she would have thought about the book she had just finished, or planned her sightseeing programme for the next day, but tonight was no ordinary night; tonight she had been kissed by Marcus Stone, and she could think of nothing else. Cordelia wasn't what might be called inexperienced; she wasn't exactly ugly and she had been kissed by many boy-friends during her twenty years, some of whom had been fairly hot stuff. But somehow they all seemed to fade into insignificance compared to what had been merely a casual kiss from Marcus. And that it had been casual on his part she was quite sure. She had let him know that she wanted to be kissed and he had obliged. It was as simple as that. End of story—except that that one kiss had been so devastating that Cordelia had wanted it to go on and on, to grow more passionate, to lead to . . .

Her body grew hot all over and she pushed aside the blanket, thin though it was. If that was only a casual kiss, what would he be like when he really meant it? The thought made her gasp and she turned restlessly on the pillow. She was being a fool. He obviously had the girl Sugin to take care of all his sexual needs, although somehow Cordelia didn't think that there were any strong emotional ties involved, not on Marcus's side in any case. Sugin was clearly possessive about him and didn't like having anyone around who might be in danger of becoming a rival—she had made that very obvious with her resentment of Cordelia. But as to whether either of them were in love . . . Perhaps if they'd been lovers for two years their feelings for each other wouldn't be so open. It was hard to tell, and a problem Cordelia had never had to face before. Moodily she turned over and let herself remember instead the feel of his lips on hers. Her fingers gripped the pillow tightly. No one had ever kissed her like that before. No one. And she would see him tomorrow. It would soon be tomorrow.

But the next day she hardly saw him at all. As was to be expected, she woke late and found that Marcus had already eaten and gone into his study, and as soon as she sat down at the table, his English-speaking driver came to ask her where she wanted to visit. Cordelia had completely forgotten that she was supposed to be spending the day sightseeing and would much rather have spent it working alongside Marcus, but he had already refused her services once and she had the sense not to insist. The last thing she wanted was for him to think that she was chasing him. So she picked out two or three places at random and the driver went off to plan the route. When she had eaten, Cordelia collected her bag and camera, said goodbye to her father, and hesitated outside Marcus's door, then decisively pushed it open.

'I just looked in to say goodbye,' she said brightly, but he was sitting at his desk and hardly looked up.

' 'Bye. Have a good day.'

'No shopping or anything you want done while I have the car?'

He looked at her then, a slightly surprised quirk in his eyebrows. 'No, nothing.'

'Okay. See you at dinner, then.'

But his eyes were already on his work again, and she shut the door feeling rather foolish.

The car was air-conditioned, but it was a hot day and the roads were so bad that Cordelia told the driver to stop in Kandy so that they could go into a restaurant and have a drink. She looked across the lake to the island where the king had been entertained by his concubines and thought of all that had happened since she had last seen it; then she had been looking forward to no more than seeing again the country of her birth, now she was to spend an indefinite time in the house of a man she found infinitely masculine and attractive and whose kisses excited her as never before. She suddenly jumped to her feet, taking her driver by surprise, eager to get the day's sightseeing over so that she could get back to the bungalow.

The driver made a conscientious guide, helping her up the steep, rock-faced hill to the temple of Dambulla that had begun as a natural cave in the rock and been patiently extended in ancient times until now it was big enough to hold dozens of statues of Buddha, with the walls and roof covered in paintings which all had some religious significance and which the driver carefully explained, holding a torch high above his head so that she could see. After the semi-darkness of the cave it hurt her eyes to come out into the full glare of the noon sun, but there were a few trees where tame monkeys played and did tricks for the titbits of food the visitors gave them. They went down the hill more slowly and Cordelia paused to give some coins to the most badly disabled of the beggars who sat on the rock in the open sun, their hands held out like the heads of cobras, waving in front of her. There were beggars everywhere, of course, not always disabled, nearly always children or poor people who saw a tourist and thought they would try their luck. More often than not the children would ask for school pens, although they were always provided with them at school. There seemed to be far more of them than she remembered, but perhaps as a child she had just accepted them and had taken little notice. The driver told her that every so often the government rounded all the beggars up and took them off to beggar colonies.

From Dambulla they drove across country to Anuradhapura, a large city built by the Buddhists in the fourth century B.C., stopping at a hotel for lunch on the way. So by the time they got there it was incredibly hot and Cordelia would have been content to drive around the city and stay in the coolness of the car, but her driver, Daya, insisted that they get out to examine every place of interest and explained everything and answered all her questions so conscientiously that she didn't have the heart to refuse. So she looked at the ruins of palaces and monasteries, at ritual baths and excavations, at huge dagobas, or temples, dome-shaped and topped by ornate steeples; she saw them as overgrown ruins, ravaged by centuries of time and weather; in the process of restoration with each brick being carefully replaced; and then restored as they had been originally, painted white and glistening in the hot sun.

Personally she preferred the mellow ruins, but Daya proudly insisted on taking her all round the restored temple. It was so hot that the heat rose in hazy waves off the concrete. At Buddhist shrines you have to take off your shoes and walk barefoot. Most Sri Lankans went barefoot all the time anyway, so their feet were hardened, but Cordelia found the sun-baked concrete so hot that she could hardly bear it and scuttled on tiptoe into even the smallest patch of shade whenever she could find one.

'We go now to see the sacred bo-tree,' Daya informed her, adding encouragingly as he saw her wilting, 'You like this very much. Very holy place. All pilgrims go there.'

Resignedly Cordelia got back into the car for another short, dusty drive and then got out again, took off her shoes and hat and listened to Daya's lecture on how the tree, that looked no different from any other as far as she could see, was an offshoot of the very tree under which Buddha achieved his enlightenment and which was over two thousand years old. Now it was housed inside a sanctuary and protected by railings topped with gold spikes. At its foot many pilgrims knelt, their heads touching the ground, while others filled little metal cups with oil and lit them, much as Roman Catholics lit candles in a church. Against one wall was a framework hung with hundreds of gaily-coloured pieces of cloth which Daya told her had been tied on to it as tokens of sacred vows that the pilgrims had made here. It was very noisy; in the distance they could hear the sound of a service being taken over a loudspeaker, there was the sort of muttering rise and fall of voices of people praying as well as the ordinary noises of the people coming and going around them. But somehow, despite all this, and as different as it was from the reverential atmosphere of an English church, Cordelia felt that here, in this noisy little square, was the heart of a living religion, far more so than the grandly restored dagobas and their huge statues of painted Buddhas.

Afterwards Daya drove her to the local rest-house, built by the British to house intrepid tourists of a much earlier age. Cordelia relaxed under the elegant white colonnades and watched the monkeys who lived in the tree-shaded grounds as she sipped a very welcome drink in a tall, frosted glass. She wondered if her father would have brought her here and how he would have described the sites of Anuradhapura to her—not very sympathetically, she decided with a small grimace, and wasn't altogether sorry that he wasn't able to come with her. But this inevitably led her to wonder what it would have been like with Marcus with his writer's eye for detail and his alert mind that could seize on the interesting or unusual. Cordelia wished very much that he had been with her, that they had shared the day together. Sightseeing really wasn't much fun unless you had someone to share it with, preferably someone you cared about.

So did that mean that she cared about Marcus? Cordelia settled back in her chair and thought about it. She certainly found him fun to be with and he had a magnetic personality that was impossible to resist, and he was so sure of himself, so self-confident. Cordelia hadn't met many men who were so positive, so vigorously masculine before, and it was hardly any wonder that he had made such an impression on her. But to care about him? When she'd only known him for a couple of days? Surely that wasn't possible? It must just be the thrill of meeting and working with someone so famous that had made her feel like this, she decided.

She was still quite sure of this on the long journey home, as she sat in the back of the car and watched the lamps being lit in the houses and tiny shops as the day gave way to dusk. Soon it grew dark and Daya had to drive more slowly, sound his horn even more often to clear the road ahead. The miles seemed to drag by as Cordelia grew more and more impatient to get home to see Marcus, to tell him about her day. She tried to remember things she'd seen that might interest or amuse him, telling herself that she was only eager to tell him because he was a writer and might be able to use them. At last they reached the hill leading down to the bungalow and she saw its welcoming lights shining out across the valley. She sat forward, her heart beating faster than it should, and somehow managed to thank Daya properly before turning to run into the bungalow to find Marcus.

But only Sugin was waiting for her inside, a Sugin who took in her eager face and searching eyes and said cruelly, 'Marcus has gone out. He decided not to wait for you. You will have to eat alone—again.' With a slight but insulting emphasis on the 'again'.

And Cordelia knew then that, even though she had only known him for a short time, she did care. She cared very much.

CHAPTER FOUR

It was very late. Glancing at her watch, Cordelia saw that it was nearly nine-thirty. It had taken them over four hours to cover the bad, crowded roads from Anuradhapura.

'You have eaten on the way?' Sugin asked her.

Cordelia shook her head. 'No, not since lunch.'

'Then I will tell them to cook you something.'

'Please don't bother, I'm quite capable of . . .'

But the other girl had already gone out into the hall and was shouting something in Sinhalese to the people in the kitchen. After a few moments she came back and said, 'I have told the cook to make you some soup and an omelette. Then he and the others can go home.' She said it as if the whole staff had been kept waiting for hours.

'Thank you,' Cordelia said stiffly. 'I will be ready to eat it in half an hour.' Going into her room, she showered and changed, finding it blissful to be cool and clean again after the hot sweatiness of the long day. Automatically she brushed her hair and put on fresh make-up, although there was no impetus to do so when Marcus wasn't going to be there. She expected Sugin to have gone when she returned to the sitting-room, but the other girl was still there and followed her into the dining-room, calmly seating herself in the place where Marcus usually sat.

'You enjoyed visiting the ancient places in Sri Lanka?' Sugin asked, her tone not in the least interested or friendly.

'Very much, thank you,' Cordelia answered after she had smilingly thanked the servant who brought her soup.

'Where did you go?' Sugin leant her elbows on the table and put a hand under her chin, watching Cordelia intently as she ate.

Briefly Cordelia told her, hating being watched in such a way.

'There are many such places to go to in Sri Lanka. You must see them all. I will give you a list.'

For a moment Cordelia was surprised at the native girl's encouragement, but then realised that it would suit Sugin for her to go out sightseeing all the time because it would keep her away from Marcus, so she just gave a small polite smile and asked, 'Where did you learn to speak English so well? Have you been to England?'

Sugin shook her head proudly. 'It is not necessary to go to a foreign country to learn the language. I learn English at school—I am very good pupil. When I leave school I have job as guide in tea factory. Then I meet Charles Conran and I come here.'

'Charles Conran is the owner of the bungalow?' Cordelia hazarded.

Sugin nodded gracefully, as she did everything gracefully. 'Yes.' She looked at Cordelia through slanted, triumphant eyes. 'And now I am—with Marcus.'

'Oh, yes,' Cordelia agreed with soft venom. 'He told me you came with the bungalow—just like the rest of the furniture.'

She hadn't intended to be spiteful, after all it was none of her business, but the other girl's gloating malevolence had so put her back up that she hadn't been able to stop herself. For a moment the barb didn't sink in, but then Sugin bristled like one of the wild leopards in the game reserves. 'You should not stay here, English girl,' she spat out, 'Marcus does not want you here. You interfere with his work. That is why he gives you the car and tells Daya to keep you out all day. This is why he goes out at night. He does not wish to be here alone with you. You bore him, English girl. He wants you to go to a hotel.'

'He does—or you do?' Cordelia demanded, aware that it was open warfare between them.

'He does! He told me so—many times,' Sugin retorted angrily.

'I don't believe you. I . . .' Cordelia broke off as the houseboy brought her omelette and took her soup dish away. Somehow it seemed ridiculous to be having this kind of argument while she was trying to eat a meal, but to push her plate away would be some sort of victory for Sugin, so she forced herself to go on eating as calmly as she could.

'It is true. He does not want you here,' Sugin insisted. 'Your father can stay because he is a sick man. But Marcus wishes that you would go.'

'Really? I must ask him, then, mustn't I?'

If Cordelia had hoped to disconcert the other girl, she was disappointed. Sugin merely shrugged and said, 'He is too polite to tell you himself, but me he has told many times. He tells me many things. We have no secrets,' she added, emphasising the words.

Cordelia didn't have to have it spelled out for her; she was fully aware that Sugin must be his mistress. As calmly as she could, she finished her meal and wiped her lips. 'I expect you want to get home. Please don't let me keep you.'

Sugin smiled and shook her head. 'I am not going home tonight. Marcus has asked me to wait for him. So you might as well go to bed, English girl. He does not want you to wait for him again tonight.'

Only Marcus could have told Sugin that she had been up when he got home last night, and Cordelia flushed, wondering for the first time if there had been any truth in the other girl's words. Maybe he really didn't want her around, even though he had assured her that she and her father could stay as long as they needed to.

Seeing that she had scored a hit, Sugin went on, 'Why do you not go home, English girl? There is nothing for you in Sri Lanka.'

Annoyed, Cordelia stood up and retorted sharply, 'On the contrary, I have just as much right to be here as you have.'

'You? What do you mean?'

'I mean that I was born here too. I'm as Sri Lankan as you are.'

Which wasn't strictly true, but at least enabled her to walk out of the room leaving Sugin completely disconcerted.

Out in the hall, Cordelia found that her hands were trembling and she had to get a grip on herself before going across to tap softly on her father's door. He was asleep, so she spent some time sitting with the nurse and chatting quietly. It was the nurse's last night, she told Cordelia. The doctor had come this morning and said that his patient was well enough to leave and that in future a nurse would just come twice a day to help him to bathe and make sure he took his pills and was generally okay. Cordelia passed a pleasant hour with her, finding the woman intelligent and friendly. She also spoke English very well and said that all children were taught it in school as a second language as a matter of course, so it wasn't such a big thing as Sugin made out that she spoke English so fluently.

It was almost midnight when Cordelia finally turned out her light and lay awake in the darkness, listening, and it must have been nearly one before she heard Marcus come home. She strained her ears, trying to hear him talking to Sugin, but they must have been very quiet, because all she heard was the sound of his door shutting softly. Perhaps Sugin was already in his room, lying naked in his bed, waiting for him to come to her, Cordelia imagined restlessly, and was seized with such a violent fit of jealousy that she could cheerfully have got hold of Sugin and strangled her. But the next second she realised miserably that she was the intruder and that Marcus probably looked on her only as a silly young girl who had thrown herself at his head. Why else would he have told Sugin about last night? Had he even told the other girl that he'd kissed her? Cordelia wondered wretchedly. Had they laughed together about it? Another sound caught her attention and she realised that it was her father's nurse going into the kitchen to make herself a drink. She, too, had been awake late last night and could have heard her talking to Marcus. Maybe it was she who had mentioned it to Sugin. Slightly comforted, Cordelia tried to go to sleep, but her mind was filled with pictures of the two of them together and, even when fatigue overcame her, her dreams, too, were about them making love, so that she turned and murmured restlessly.

Next morning, she had to use make-up to

disguise the dark smudges of tiredness around her eyes. She wasn't looking forward to having to face the two of them, especially knowing that they had spent the night together; she could imagine the way Sugin would look at her with triumph in her dark eyes, the possessive way she would preside over the breakfast table, every movement calculated to emphasise the fact that she was not only Marcus's mistress but also virtually the mistress of his house and that Cordelia was only an unwanted interloper. And Marcus? Would his night of love show in his face, in his manner? Cordelia gripped her hairbrush and bit her lip hard. There was only one way, she decided, that she was going to get through today, and that was by acting as if he really was just her boss, by being brisk and impersonal and definitely not letting him see that she fancied him. Even so, she took as long as she could over getting ready, but she couldn't hang around in her room for ever, so eventually she went out on to the verandah.

To her surprise only Marcus was there, reading a letter from a small pile beside his plate. He stood up as she came out, his eyes running fleetingly over her.

'Good morning. How did you enjoy your sightseeing?'

Acting on her decision, she gave him a bright smile and answered, 'It was very interesting, thank you. Daya was a very good guide. We went to Dambulla and then on to Anuradhapura.'

'What did you think of them?'

Cordelia remembered all the interesting things she had stored up to tell him and resolutely pushed them aside. 'As I said, they were very interesting. Please don't let me stop you if you were reading your mail,' she added, and pointedly looked away to butter a piece of toast.

Marcus smiled lazily. 'Are you the type that prefers to start the morning in peace and quite? Who bury themselves in the morning paper to avoid having to make conversation over the coffee and toast?'

Shrugging her shoulders, Cordelia said, 'I don't know, really. I only ever eat breakfast when I'm on holiday; I don't bother with it when I'm at home.'

'Where's home?'

'I share a flat near Baker Street with three other girls.'

'And you work in an office, I think you said?'

'Yes.'

'What do you do in your leisure time?'

She shrugged again. 'We go to discos and the cinema quite a lot—and I'm taking a course of evening classes to learn book-keeping.'

'Very commendable,' Marcus commented on an amused note, then his voice changed as he said, 'No boy-friends?'

Cordelia choked a little over her coffee but managed to cover it with a cough. His eyes settled on her, but she didn't meet them. 'One or two.' She managed to say it offhandedly, then immediately put down her coffee cup and stood up. 'I expect you'd like me to start work now; I still have a lot to do before I catch up with you.'

Without waiting for him to answer, she walked along the verandah and went into the study, where she began to take the cover off the typewriter; the conversation had started to get too personal if she was to be able to stay brisk and businesslike. Marcus followed more slowly. He stood watching her for a moment, then remarked, 'You're very efficient this morning.'

'Am I? Well, there's a lot to do.'

'Is anything the matter?'

She allowed herself a brief glance in his direction. 'No, of course not. Why should there be?' She sat down and pulled his manuscript forward. 'What chapter did you get up to yesterday?'

'Chapter six.'

'Then you're still four ahead of me.'

His hand came down on to her shoulder and she had to stifle a gasp as his touch seemed to burn into her flesh. 'This isn't a race, you know,' he remarked gently.

Cordelia stiffened but didn't look up. Licking lips gone suddenly dry, she managed to say brightly, 'Oh, but I'm eager to read the rest of the book.'

His hand stayed where it was a moment longer, then he took it away and sat down at his desk. He didn't say anything further; after such a silly remark as hers there probably wasn't anything to say. Cordelia began to type and after a while had to take the sheet out of the machine when he wasn't looking because she'd made so many mistakes.

They worked on through the morning and when Marcus stopped for coffee she didn't take it with him but excused herself and went to see her father. When she came back there was a slightly sardonic curl to his mouth, but Marcus merely asked after the invalid.

'He seems much better, thank you. He's going to get up for a while this afternoon.'

'Good. I'm glad to hear he's making progress.'

Because then we'll be gone the sooner? Cordelia wondered. So that he can be alone with Sugin again. There had been no sign of the other girl this morning, but Cordelia was fully expecting her to put in an appearance at lunchtime and was agreeably surprised when she saw that the table had been set for only two. Perhaps Sugin was still recovering from last night, she thought, with a flash of emotion which was as much jealousy as bitchiness. Not that Marcus's face showed any sign of tiredness or dissipation; she studied him covertly as she ate, listening as he talked about the chapter of the book he was working on. Her eyes ran over his aggressively handsome features, the wide breadth of his shoulders, and lingered on the play of the muscles in his bare, tanned arms. She wondered what he would be like in bed.

Almost as if she had said the words aloud, Marcus suddenly fell silent and looked at her. Their eyes met and held and Cordelia felt her face suffuse with colour, so that if there had been any doubt in his mind before about what she was thinking, there was certainly none now. Hastily she looked away and began to eat feverishly. The silence seemed to go on for ever, but at last he began to talk again, picking up from where he had left off. But the amusement in his voice was quite clear. Damn you, Cordelia swore inwardly. Stop laughing at me, damn you! She didn't dare look at him in case she blushed again, and luckily he didn't ask her any questions, just went on talking easily until they had finished and went back to work again.

Somehow she managed to pull herself together and get through the rest of the afternoon and dinner, but gave a sigh of relief when Marcus

afterwards went in to sit with her father and she
was able to go to her room with a book and not
see him any more that night. He had offered her
the car again for another sightseeing trip the next
day, but the driver had reported that there was a
part that needed replacing and had taken it to a
garage which promised it back in two days. 'But
knowing Sri Lankan garages it could be anything
up to two weeks,' Marcus had remarked wryly.

The next two days were better; Cordelia was
more in control of herself, had managed to get
things back in proportion and was able to keep the
hours they were alone together on an impersonal
but friendly level, if such a thing were possible.
Marcus went along with it, although once or twice
she found him watching her with that sardonically
amused look on his lean features. After dinner
they both went in to sit with James Allingham and
had a game of gin rummy with him. Cordelia was
amazed at the way her father's personality
changed when he was with Marcus; he talked far
more than he ever did with her, especially when
Marcus drew him out on his years managing the
tea plantation, and he even laughed a few times at
his own experiences. Perhaps it was that he
preferred men's company, Cordelia surmised, and
excused herself quite early on the plea of being
tired, hoping that he would expand even more
without her presence to restrict him.

On the third day they had breakfasted and
Cordelia had started work when Marcus stepped
briskly into the room, swung her chair round and
pulled her to her feet. 'No work today! Contrary
to my pessimistic view the car's been repaired as
promised and you're taking the day off.'

'Oh, but I was in the middle of . . .' She went to

sit down again, but he kept hold of her wrists and wouldn't let her.

'Oh, no, you don't. You heard me—we're going sightseeing.'

Cordelia stared at him. 'We?'

'Yes. It's Daya's day off, so I'm afraid you'll have to put up with me as your guide.' His eyes glinted down into hers. 'Do you mind?'

Her heart began to beat much too fast and her throat was so dry that she stammered as she said, 'N-no, of course not.'

'Good.' He smiled down at her, his mouth slightly more curved one side than the other, which stupidly made her heart give a crazy lurch. 'You have twenty minutes to get ready.' Then he was gone and she heard him giving orders to someone in the kitchen. For a few minutes she stood still, too overwhelmed by surprise, excitement and anticipation to do anything but stare after him. All her good resolutions about being brisk and impersonal had evaporated into thin air, dissolved into nothing before the word we—'We are going sightseeing.' Sugin might not have existed, the affair between them be only a figment of her imagination. Nothing mattered except that she and Marcus were going to spend the day together.

Poking his head back into the room, Marcus saw her still standing there and said with mock severity, 'Fifteen minutes!'

Cordelia suddenly came to life. Laughing happily, she covered the typewriter and ran to change into a pale blue sundress that matched her eyes and a pair of wedge-heeled, comfortable sandals. Grabbing up her bag and the other things she needed for the day, she ran out to the front of the house, a faint flush on her cheeks and all the excitement she felt showing in her eyes.

Marcus looked up from stowing a hamper in the boot of the car, an arrested expression on his face. 'You look like a child who's been promised a treat.'

Cordelia smiled at him fully for the first time in three days. 'I feel like one,' she told him happily. 'Where are we going?'

'Get in and I'll show you on the map.'

He had a big map of the island and as he sat next to her he handed it to her and helped her to spread it out on her lap. Leaning across, he pointed out the route he intended to take. 'You covered most of the road when you went with Daya, but today we're turning off to Sigiriya— here.' He pointed with a long finger. 'There's plenty of time, we don't have to rush, so if you see anywhere on the way that you want to stop and look at, just give a yell.'

'Yes, all right.' Her eyes weren't on the map but on his profile, following the hard outline of his face, her nostrils full of his freshly applied aftershave. It had a musky tang to it that made her want to get closer.

The day was hot and sunny and, as usual, the roads were full of people, but Marcus took his time and didn't drive on his brakes as Daya did, so that she didn't have to keep grabbing at the dashboard to steady herself. They stopped at a level-crossing to wait for the train to go by and where there was a big open market full of people, most of the sellers with their wares carried in on their backs and displayed in baskets or spread out on the ground on pieces of sacking. There were spiky pineapples and the rich purple sheen of mangosteens and the brilliant scarlet of chilli peppers that had been dried in the sun. But above everything was the noise of the people as they haggled loudly over their purchases, carrying umbrellas to guard them from the sun and the occasional monsoon shower. The train came along, old and dirty and packed with people, and the gates swung open. For a while the road ran alongside the single railway track, which was almost as busy as the road, with the people walking along it using it as a short cut to the next village, and with much less chance of being knocked down and killed, Cordelia guessed wryly as she watched them.

They stopped for her to take photos of an ornate painted Hindu temple covered with carvings of figures that each seemed to have an unbelievable number of arms and heads, and again at a batik factory where they were shown the waxing and dyeing processes and where Cordelia tried on and bought several dresses that had the most beautiful designs and were incredibly cheap. She had thought that Marcus might get impatient with her for spending so long in the batik shop, but he wasn't in the least; he even picked out a couple of dresses for her to try on which he said he thought would suit her. Needless to say, she bought them both.

Back in the car, Marcus drove northwards again, through an open plain with occasional villages scattered alongside the main road, with beyond them a few cultivated fields before the scrublike-looking trees that Marcus told her was the start of what the Sri Lankans called the jungle area, although it was so very open and sparse that Cordelia would never have described it as that herself. Every now and again there were huge outcrops of rock sticking up out of the plain like giant-size versions of the anthills that she saw at the sides of the road. Pointing ahead, Marcus said, 'See that huge circular rock with the flat top up ahead? That's Sigiriya where we're heading. They call it the Lion Rock.'

The rock was massive, more like a small mountain; it rose red-gold from its surrounding belt of trees to stand sentinel against the blue of the cloudless sky. When they neared it they had to stop and buy tickets before they could go any farther, but Marcus refused the services of a guide and drove on to park the car under the shade of some trees.

'I thought we might have a stroll round the ruins of the summer palace first, then have lunch and a rest before we attempt the climb up the rock. Okay by you?'

'Mm, fine.' Cordelia followed him out of the car, perfectly happy to go anywhere he cared to suggest. They wandered slowly round the ruins under the hot sun, Marcus pointing out where the different parts of the palace had stood. The day was very still and sultry and the only other people exploring the ruins were a long way off, near the foot of the Lion Rock. Cordelia had a feeling of timelessness, when she stood still and half closed her eyes she could almost see the ancient people who had inhabited these vast ruins.

'What are you thinking?' Marcus's soft question brought her out of her reverie.

'Oh, nothing really.'

'Nothing?' His eyebrows lifted in disbelief.

'Well,' she gave a half embarrassed laugh, 'only that if you closed your eyes you could imagine what it must have been like—the people who lived here then, the way it must have been.'

She expected him to laugh at her, or worse, see that sardonically mocking look in his face, but to her surprise he nodded and said quickly, 'That's right, there's an aura about the place. You can see the king sitting in his throne room, his warriors about him and dozens of the most beautiful women dancing for him and attending to his needs.'

Cordelia smiled. 'I hadn't imagined the bit about the beautiful women.'

Marcus laughed and slipped a casual arm round her waist. 'But at least you have an imagination. The last people I brought here just said, "Oh, yes" politely to everything I pointed out and couldn't wait to get to the nearest hotel with a bar.'

'Who was that?' Cordelia asked, warm from his praise and his touch.

'Oh, just some people who came over for a short visit from England.' He paused and looked away from her, was silent for a few minutes, then said almost to himself, 'I suppose that's really all they are—just a lot of old stones. Unless you have the imagination to clothe them in history.' He turned to Cordelia and let his eyes run over her tall, youthfully slim figure. 'As you have,' he said softly.

Cordelia gazed at him, sensing that there was something deeper behind his words, waiting, longing for him to go on, to confide in her, but then his eyebrows flickered at the imperative honking of a tourist coach on the nearby road and the moment was lost. He grinned at her and caught hold of her hand. 'But I bet right now you'd much rather have a glass of chilled white wine.'

'Did you say *chilled*? Just lead me to it!' Cordelia agreed fervently, and let him run her along to the car, protesting laughingly, 'You didn't mean it, did you? You haven't really got cold wine?'

But he had. He opened up the picnic hamper and revealed two bottles of wine in a special container to keep them cool.

'You,' Cordelia informed him in awestruck tones, 'are definitely the man I would most like to be marooned on a desert island with. You get my vote every time!' He passed her a glass and she drank it slowly, savouring every drop, letting it linger in her dry throat and passing her tongue over her lips. 'Oh, that was good,' she sighed reverently. 'The best drink I've ever tasted. Nectar!'

'The drink of the gods.' He took the empty glass from her and said softly, 'Your lips are wet with wine. They make me want to taste them.'

'D-do they?' Cordelia breathed, her heart standing still.

'Yes.' And he bent forward and put his mouth on hers, softly, gently, letting his lips explore its full softness, then he drew back and looked down into her rapt face. Slowly Cordelia opened her eyes; only their mouths had touched and yet she felt as if he had touched and explored her whole body, every nerve end was on fire and her heart now was racing crazily. Marcus refilled her glass and gave it to her, then filled his own and raised it. 'To all the ancient pagan gods,' he toasted, his eyes smiling lazily into hers.

'Especially to Bacchus,' Cordelia added, trying to keep her tone as light as his.

'Most definitely,' Marcus agreed with a grin. 'Now what have they given us to eat?'

So they sat in the shade of the trees in that ancient place and ate and drank, taking their time, talking and laughing often. Somehow Cordelia found herself telling him all about her life in Sri Lanka, and then back in England alone with her mother and aunt, not realising that she was betraying a great deal more to him than just her words conveyed. Then she asked him about himself, but he again evaded the question. 'Maybe one day I'll write my autobiography and you'll be able to read it all,' he told her, lying back in the grass, his head pillowed on his arms.

'Afraid I'll reveal all the sordid details of your life to the gutter press, huh?' Cordelia teased him. She stretched out alongside him, lying on her stomach, her head propped up on her elbows.

His lips curled into that slightly crooked grin. 'Watch it, woman, or I'll put you in my autobiography!'

'Really?' Cordelia was intrigued. 'What would you say?'

He had closed his eyes, but now he opened them a little and looked at her lazily. 'Well, that would depend.'

'On what?'

'On whether or not you're going to kiss me, of course.'

Cordelia had been toying idly with the gold necklace she wore, but now her fingers grew still as she stared down at him, not sure whether he was teasing or serious. But he merely gave a small grin and closed his eyes again, which was no help at all. She looked down at his face for several minutes, noticing how the lock of dark hair that had fallen forward on his forehead softened the hardness of his features. And there was a small cleft in his chin which made her want to run her finger along it. Slowly she edged a little nearer. His breathing was quite regular and she thought he had fallen asleep, so she was quite safe. Even in repose there was a harsh look to his mouth and she saw now that they were lines of bitterness that had given it that slightly sardonic curve. Cordelia found that she very much wanted to kiss those lines away, to make them disappear for ever. She leaned over him, confident that he was asleep, her eyes studying his face. Slowly she lowered her head and just touched his lips with her own, the pressure no greater than the flutter of a butterfly's wing. But even so, Marcus had felt it, and when she went to lift her head away he put a hand behind her neck so that she couldn't move. His eyes opened and looked into hers. 'You can do better than that,' he told her softly.

'Yes.' The word was no more than a sigh.

'Then show me.'

She lowered her head again, her hair falling forward and forming a golden curtain around their heads. Her lips found his and touched them gently in small kisses, each of which was a caress, demanding nothing but giving freely of their warmth and softness. He lay there, letting her take his mouth, but when Cordelia parted his lips with her tongue she felt a quiver run through him, his hand tightened on her neck and he began to kiss her passionately in return. Pulled off balance, she fell against him and immediately Marcus's arm went round her, holding her close, half lying on top of him. Cordelia's arms went round his neck as she responded, overwhelmed by his sudden

passion, lost to everything around her. But then
Marcus abruptly pushed her away and sat up and
she became aware of voices nearby. A party of Sri
Lankan pilgrims headed by two Buddhist monks
in their saffron robes were walking through the
ruins towards them. Cordelia gave them one
glance, then turned back to stare at Marcus, her
hair dishevelled, chest heaving, her eyes still
bemused with passion.

Marcus's eyes settled on her face for a long
moment, then he quickly got to his feet and pulled
her up beside him. 'Let's go up to the fortress. It
should be a little cooler now.'

Cordelia put up a hand to push the hair away
from her face, a hand that wasn't quite steady.
'Yes. All right.' She helped him to pack up the
picnic things and stow them in the car, acting
mechanically, her mind still lost in the clouds.

Marcus drove to the car park at the foot of the
Lion Rock and they walked up the path between
the little souvenir stalls selling ebony Buddhas,
brightly-coloured balsa-wood masks and beaten
brassware. They paused near a huge overhanging
rock while Marcus told her how the Buddhists had
taken over the place after the king who built the
fortress had been defeated in battle. But she wasn't
really listening; she was aware only of sensations:
of the sun hot on her back, the murmur of his
voice, of a lizard that crouched on a stone,
watching her, most of all of Marcus's closeness, his
shoulder almost touching hers; she only had to
move a few inches and she would be able to lean
against him, feel the length of his body against her
own. She quivered, the desire so great that it
became physical. Marcus's voice trailed off,
Cordelia turned her head to look at him and their

eyes met and held. She couldn't read his face, but
hers must have been plain enough, because he
smiled a little, then lifted a finger and lightly
touched her lips. 'Later,' he murmured.

They moved on up through the trees and began
to climb up the steps, Marcus acting as guide.
Then the way became steep and narrow, with only
a handrail between the path and a sheer drop
down the side of the rock. And to reach the cave
paintings they had to go up a spiral metal staircase
attached to the bare rock face. The frescoes were
rather disappointing, just a few paintings were left
where once there had been hundreds. They were
all of native girls, painted from the waist up in
gentle orange, pink and green colours. They were
adorned with jewelled headdresses, necklaces and
countless bracelets, and they all had beautifully
rounded, and quite bare, breasts.

'They call them the Cloud Maidens,' Marcus
told her. 'Because we're so high up, I suppose.'

'I don't see any paintings of men,' Cordelia
noted drily.

'Of course not. These ancient kings knew how to
get their priorities right.'

'You mean they date from the Early Chauvinist
Age?'

Marcus's laugh echoed round the shallow cave
in which they stood. Putting a hand on her arm, he
said, 'You know, you make me realise what I've
been missing while I've been here.'

Cordelia didn't ask him to explain. To see him
smile, to feel his hand on her arm, was enough.
She felt as high as the Cloud Maidens, her heart
soaring dizzily. They went back down the spiral
stairs and Marcus helped her because she wasn't
that good on heights. She was terribly aware of

him, every time he touched her, even of his closeness; it was as if there was some sort of electric current running between them that set off sparks every time they touched.

Walking round to the other side of the rock they came to a place where once the massive head of a lion crouching on its paws had stood guard over the entrance to the upper fortress on top of the rock. Now only the paws remained on either side of some steps that had once gone through the archway of the lion's mouth. Above the steps there was an iron ladder with a handrail attached to the rock face.

'Do you want to try it?' Marcus asked her.

Cordelia hesitated as she looked up the sheer climb. 'Have you ever been up there?' she asked doubtfully.

'Yes. But don't try it if you'd rather not.'

She gulped. 'I'll try.'

Going up the first part wasn't too bad, but then there was a tricky place which was just narrow, worn footsteps in the granite with only a low handrail to hold on to, but Marcus put a firm hand on her arm and she was up before she knew it. On the very top of the rock there were more ruins, and they wandered round for an hour or so, exploring. Then they had to get down. Cordelia found this a hundred times worse because you could see the drop below, and there was one really nasty moment when some people coming up wanted to pass. Almost she panicked, but Marcus put his arm round her, talking to her matter-of-factly, and somehow the other people were past and they were safely down to the lion's paws again.

Marcus sat her down and went over to a drinks

stall under a tree which described itself as a 'Cool Spot' and brought her back a Coke. 'Here. 'Fraid it's not very cold, though.'

'Oh, *thanks*!' Cordelia drank thirstily and put up a hand to wipe the perspiration from her brow.

'You were scared stiff during that climb, weren't you?' Marcus observed accusingly. And when she nodded, he went on, 'So why did you do it?'

She shrugged. 'Because I wanted to get to the top. I didn't want to be beaten.'

He looked amused. 'And do you always go after what you want so determinedly? Even though you're afraid?'

Cordelia set down the empty bottle of Coke and said lightly, 'I suppose that depends on how badly I want something. Aren't you willing to take a risk if you want something badly enough?'

His eyes rested on her face, flushed from the climb, and he nodded. 'Yes. And I always get what I want.'

'Always?'

'Yes. Always,' he answered firmly.

'How spoilt you must be, then,' Cordelia observed, wrinkling her nose at him.

He laughed, 'Hopelessly!' and reached out to take her hand and lead her back down the hill.

They didn't hurry on the drive back to the bungalow. Nor did they hurry over dinner afterwards, but both of them were aware of the physical tension and of the word 'later' that lay between them. They chatted easily over the meal, like people who had known each other a long time. Cordelia had pushed Sugin's shadow far into the background; she hadn't seen the other girl for three days and she certainly wasn't going to ask where she was. Occasionally, accidentally—or almost accidentally—their hands would touch, and Cordelia would almost gasp aloud. She had never before known such desire, such intense physical need.

When they had finished, Marcus stood up. 'Let's go for a stroll round the garden, shall we?' He took her hand and together they walked across the verandah and down into the warm scented garden.

They walked on until they had outdistanced the light thrown by the lamps in the house and there was only the moonlight to guide them. Marcus paused near the frangipani tree, its white flowers luminous in the soft rays of the moonlight. Leaning against the trunk of the tree, he pulled her gently towards him. 'Cordelia,' he breathed, his arms going round her, 'how lovely you look! So fair, so very fair.' He kissed her gently at first, then lifted his head to watch the moonlight play on the golden silk of her hair as he let it run through his fingers.

Cordelia stood it for as long as she could, but the touch of his fingers drove her mad. She dug her fingers into his shoulders and said his name on a little moan of need. 'Marcus.' He gave a low chuckle and put his hands down low on her hips, pulling her against him so that she gasped at his hardness. Then his mouth was on hers, fierce and demanding, and she surrendered happily to his blazing passion.

He kissed her again and again, his lips finding her eyes, her throat, setting her blood on fire. His hands went to her shoulders and pulled down the thin straps of her dress so that it hung from the belt at her waist. He tried to push her away a little so that he could look at her, but Cordelia clung to him, wanting to stay close. Firmly, then, he took hold of her hands so that she had to reluctantly move a step backwards. His eyes dwelt on the curve of her breasts, shadowed by the moonlight. 'You're beautiful,' he breathed thickly. 'Perfect. Like the Cloud Maidens.' Lifting his hands, he cupped her breasts, caressed them so that they hardened as she gasped with delight.

'But I'm real. I'm alive,' she managed to say, and impatiently pulled his head down to kiss him. She didn't give a damn about the Cloud Maidens, all she wanted was for Marcus to go on kissing and caressing her and never, ever stop. His lips took hers hungrily and then moved down to her breasts, making her give low, animal moans of pleasure. 'Oh, my darling,' she gasped. 'My love, my love!' His breath seemed to scorch her skin and she pressed herself against him, his hardness driving her crazy with longing. Putting his arms round her, Marcus held her still, her head against the hammering beat of his heart. When she tried to move he wouldn't let her, made her stay still for several long minutes, until his heart had retained a normal beat and her pulses had stopped racing quite so much.

Lifting her head at last, Cordelia looked at him questioningly. 'Marcus?'

He didn't answer, merely kissed her lightly on the forehead, slipped her dress back on her shoulders and then put his arm round her waist and led her back through the garden towards the house. Cordelia went with him willingly, her heart large and unruly in its beat. Her eyes were brilliant in her flushed face, as if lit from within, and she could think of nothing but the present, the here and now of being with Marcus, of feeling his arm around her, of going wherever he wanted to take her. And she fully expected that he was taking her to his bed. Short of him throwing her down on the ground, they had gone about as far as they could go, out there in the garden. It was natural now that he should take her back to the house, back to the nearest bed. The thought filled her with shy, excited anticipation, but no shame. The searing emotion and need he had aroused in her had been too intense for that. She wanted him as much as he seemed to want her. Never before had she experienced such a need for fulfilment, the urgent craving to be taken by a man—no, not any man, just this man, no one else.

She stumbled a little as they went up the steps to the verandah and Marcus's arm tightened round her waist. Cordelia laughed rather raggedly. 'My legs seem to have turned to jelly!'

He paused and looked down at her, a small frown between his dark brows. 'Cordelia, I . . .' His voice held a slightly troubled note, but he was unable to go on because Cordelia put her arms round his neck and leant her weight against him.

'I'm afraid you'll have to hold me up; my legs have no strength at all. You see what you've done to me?' she added with another excited laugh. Her grip tightened and her voice grew husky with emotion. 'Oh, Marcus. Darling, dearest Marcus! Today has been such a wonderful day. I shall never forget it, not as long as I live.'

Reaching up, he took her hands from round his neck, held them as his face, dark in the shadowed night, looked down into hers. Then he gently bent to kiss her lips, almost, Cordelia thought strangely, as if with regret or sadness.

'You must be tired. You'd better go in.'

'Yes.' She went ahead of him for a few steps, then turned. 'Aren't you—aren't you coming in too?' It was as close as she could get to an invitation, the nearest thing to saying, 'I want you to take me to your bed. I want you to love me.'

He seemed to murmur something under his breath, something she didn't catch, and she hadn't the courage to ask him again. He stood, a tall, dark shadow against the darker shadow of the night, unmoving, waiting for her to go. Quickly Cordelia turned on her heel and almost ran to her room. She prepared for bed eagerly, putting on her newest nightdress, brushing her hair until it shone, her hands trembling, her body aching for him. Turning off the lights, she left only a small lamp burning and opened her door on to the verandah in case he came that way.

But he didn't come. She waited until the house had been quiet for a long time before she turned off the light and got into bed. But even though the physical disappointment was intense, she wasn't unhappy. It had all happened so fast, like a carousel whirling round out of control, perhaps it was better this way. After all, they had plenty of time, all the time in the world. There was tomorrow, and all the tomorrows after that when they would be together. The future stretched into infinity and Cordelia smiled as she drifted into sleep.

CHAPTER FIVE

As usual, Marcus was up before her, even though Cordelia got up as soon as she awoke. He was sitting at the breakfast table, reading the local paper, and looked up when he heard her quick footsteps. She gave him a wonderful smile, her heart on her face, her blue eyes alight with happiness. 'Good morning.'

'Good morning.' He put down the paper and poured her a cup of coffee. 'You look very well this morning.'

'I feel well. I feel terrific.' She smiled again, her eyes warm as they dwelt almost hungrily on his face. 'You know I do.'

A brief frown covered his forehead, but then the houseboy came to bring her breakfast, and when she looked again the frown had gone. Marcus stood up. 'Would you excuse me? I have some telephoning to do.'

He was gone some time; she'd finished eating and had looked at the paper by the time he came back. She got quickly to her feet. 'I'm ready to start work.'

'Don't you think you ought to go and see how your father is? You hardly saw him yesterday,' Marcus reminded her.

'Oh, yes, of course. I'll be right back.' She laughed up at him and touched his hand. 'Don't start without me.'

James Allingham was seated in a chair by the window, playing a game of patience. For once he seemed quite pleased to see her and even asked her about her trip to Sigiriya, telling her about a visit he had made to it about thirty years ago. Cordelia listened as patiently as she could, while all the time longing to get back to Marcus. At length she cut her father short, explaining that their host was waiting for her to do some typing for him. It was near enough the truth. She hurried from his room without regret; her father had dismissed her enough in the past week for her to feel it.

Marcus was working at his desk, his back towards her as she slipped into the room. Quietly, an impish smile on her lips, Cordelia crept up behind him and put her hands over his eyes. 'Guess who?' she breathed.

He half turned round and lifted up an arm to pull her hands away, but Cordelia slipped on to his lap, leaving one arm round his neck and with the other gently tracing the outline of his lips with her finger. Then she kissed him, lingeringly, reliving all over again the thrill of his mouth on hers.

He didn't respond, but he didn't draw away either; just let her go on kissing him, and when she looked at him with questioning doubt, only gave that crooked grin and said, 'Delightful as that sort of thing can be, young lady, it isn't helping to get this book finished.'

Slowly she stood up. 'You—you mean there's a time and a place for everything?'

'Something like that.' He swung back to his desk and bent his head to his work again.

Cordelia went to her own desk and stared at his bent head. She felt like a teenager who'd tried to do something grown up, only to be told that she was still a child. Didn't he feel the same as she did?

She wanted to be near him, to touch, to see him, and she didn't care where or what time of the day it was. To confirm all that yesterday, and especially last night, had meant to her. Unless it had all meant nothing to him. But surely not. He couldn't have kissed her like that without it meaning anything at all. She had to know, had to ask him. 'Marcus . . .' she began.

But he cut in at once, his voice brusque. 'I've put the next chapter to be typed just by the typewriter.'

After a long pause, Cordelia picked up a piece of paper and put it in the machine, then began to type.

Just before lunch, there was the sound of a car outside and Marcus went out to see who it was. He came back with another man, younger than himself, perhaps in his late twenties; a tall man with brown hair bleached by the sun and a darkly tanned body revealed by his short-sleeved shirt that was open to the waist of his tight-fitting jeans.

'Cordelia, this is Steve Randall. He's working up on the dam they're building up in the hills. You remember, I told you about it.'

'Yes, of course. How do you do, Mr Randall?'

The young man laughed. 'You're very formal! We all call one another by our Christian names out here.'

'Let's go outside and have a drink before lunch.' Marcus led the way out on to the verandah and they sat at the white-painted table while they waited for the houseboy to bring the drinks.

'Marcus told us all about the accident you had,' Steve told her. 'How is your father now?'

'Recovering quite well, thank you.' Cordelia

wished the man wasn't there, wished Marcus didn't seem so pleased to see him.

'Must have given you quite a fright. Has the doc said when he'll be well enough to be moved?'

'No, not yet. He had a heart attack, you see; that's what made him crash,' she felt impelled to add. Her eyes kept going to Marcus, but he was looking down at his drink.

Steve started asking her about her life in England and it became apparent that he expected to stay to lunch. From his talk with Marcus she gathered that he was one of his friends from the Expatriates Club and that on the evenings Marcus went there they mostly played poker or some other card game. But he didn't talk to Marcus too much, most of his attention he gave to Cordelia, telling her about the dam he was working on, with some really funny anecdotes about the differences and misunderstandings that often arose with the native labour force. 'Sometimes, when I shout at them for being too slow or for doing something stupidly dangerous,' he told her, 'they refuse to do any more work. Then we send for *my* boss, who's another Englishman, and he pretends to shout at me for shouting at *them*, and that makes them happy again and they all go back to work.'

Marcus grinned and encouraged him to go on. He took little part in the conversation himself, which was unusual; not that Cordelia said very much, she merely smiled and put in suitable remarks and questions at appropriate moments. Every other minute her eyes would go back to Marcus, seeing some sign, some acceptance from him of their closer involvement. A look that was for her alone, a smile, a touch of hands, even a wink would have lifted her back into the clouds.

Once their eyes did meet and he did smile, but it was a casual, impersonal smile, meaning nothing. If he had deliberately looked away, avoided her eyes, Cordelia would have known that something was wrong and she could have tried to do something about it, but against apparent indifference she was completely helpless.

When they had finished lunch and were lingering over coffee, Steve said to Marcus, 'Where's Sugin? I haven't seen her around today.'

'Her sister is ill. She's gone to look after her for a few days.'

'Her sister doesn't live over at her mother's place, then?'

'No, her sister's married and lives over in Nuwara Eliya,' Marcus answered dismissively.

So Steve knew all about Sugin, and presumably that she was Marcus's mistress, Cordelia realised unhappily. Since last night she hadn't given much thought to Sugin, but now she began to wonder if it was because of her that Marcus seemed so offhand. Had he just been amusing himself with her while Sugin wasn't around? And had he now decided that he preferred the other girl? He ought to, she supposed, trying to be realistic; after all, theirs had been a much longer relationship.

'What places have you visited in Sri Lanka, Cordelia?' Steve's voice interrupted her thoughts and she was forced to concentrate on answering him.

'Have you been to Colombo yet?' She admitted that she hadn't and he immediately said, 'Hey, why don't we go over there this afternoon? We could see the sights and then we could go over to the Intercontinental to swim and then have dinner there.' He looked at them both eagerly. 'How about it? If we left now we could be in Colombo in a couple of hours. You'd like to go, wouldn't you, Cordelia?'

Cordelia didn't, not in the least. 'I've been helping Marcus with his work,' she temporised. 'I know he wants to get on.'

'Nonsense, you're on holiday,' said Marcus. 'And you ought to see Colombo.' He paused for a moment, then glanced at Steve. 'I think it's a great idea. Let's all go.' He got to his feet and looked down at her. 'Cordelia?'

'Yes, okay. Give me ten minutes to get ready.'

She hurried to her room, grateful that Marcus hadn't tried to push her off on to Steve. For a few moments back there she had been certain that that was what he intended to do, that he would make work his excuse to stay behind. But if he had, she wouldn't have gone, she would have insisted on staying to help him. She started to wonder if Steve had been invited over just to take her off Marcus's hands, and the thought chilled her through to her bones.

They went in Marcus's car, it having been chosen as more comfortable for her than the Land Rover Steve had borrowed from the dam workings, which meant that Marcus drove with Cordelia in the front seat beside him and Steve leaning forward in the space between the seats, his arms reaching along their backs. Cordelia hadn't travelled along the road before, so there were plenty of places of interest for Steve to point out to her, including a mountain known as Adam's Peak.

'You'll have to go and see that, Cordelia,' Steve enthused. 'You have to get to the top before dawn because then a bank of clouds blows into the valley below and for a brief moment the sun catches it and somehow casts the shadow of the mountain on to the mass of clouds. It's almost like a—what do you call those things they have in the desert?'

'A mirage,' Marcus supplied.

'Yeah, that's right.'

'Or an illusion,' Cordelia added drily.

Marcus shot her a quick look under hooded lids, but Steve innocently assured her, 'No, you can see it all right, it's really there.'

'Have you seen it?' She made an effort to keep the conversation going—after all, it wasn't Steve's fault that there was this tension building up in her.

'No, but some of the other men have. They say it's well worth making the effort to go there. Why don't we go and see it together?' he suggested.

Cordelia didn't know whether the 'we' included Marcus, but she said lightly anyway, 'Why not?' having no intention of going with him. If she had been alone with Marcus, then yes, oh yes; it would have been a magical experience, but she didn't want to go with anyone else, even somebody as well-intentioned as Steve.

When they reached Colombo, they stopped for a drink and then Marcus drove her round the city so that she could see the reproduction of the giant standing statue of Buddha at Aukana, the imposing monument to Mrs Bandaranaike given to Sri Lanka by the People's Republic of China, and the television station given to the people of Sri Lanka by Japan.

'So that they'd buy Japanese television sets,' Marcus remarked sourly. They drove through streets even more crowded and chaotic than any she'd seen before and honked imperatively at little three-wheeled, two-seater electric taxis with canopies like a pram that you could put up when it rained. They passed the rose-pink buildings, known as the Fort, that covered a whole block and housed Colombo's principal shopping centre, then Marcus drove into the forecourt of the nearby Intercontinental Hotel.

They were all glad to get there and with one accord headed for the bar.

'This country always makes me feel so dry,' Cordelia commented. 'I'm always thirsty.'

'Me too,' Steve agreed, looking with loving anticipation at the huge glass of cold beer the bartender was pouring for him. He sat on a bar stool next to her and Marcus moved to her other side. For a while they just sat and drank in grateful silence, then Cordelia's bare arm happened to touch Marcus's elbow and she began to tremble as if she'd been scorched. She couldn't look at him, was afraid to, in case he saw the desolation in her face, so she determinedly turned to Steve and began to talk to him animatedly, although for the life of her afterwards she couldn't think what it was about.

When they had finished their drinks, they changed into swimsuits and walked down to the nearby beach to bathe. There was some tide and rolling waves, but they weren't very rough and it was comfortable to swim there. Cordelia wasn't that good and stayed within her depth, but the two men raced each other far out. She watched them and had visions of sharks and cramp, and breathed a sigh of relief when they came back safely. They all began to play around in the surf, chasing one another and diving down under the waves. Once Steve went under the water and caught hold of her legs, trying to duck her, but Cordelia kicked free and knifed away, but bumped into Marcus who was behind her. His arms went round her to prevent her from going under and for a moment she lay against him, their bodies touching. He looked beautiful stripped nearly naked as he was, not as obviously beefy as Steve perhaps, but tanned and muscular and athletic, with strong legs and a slim waist beneath the breadth of his shoulders. And there was a mat of dark hairs on his chest where the water clung in glistening drops. Cordelia wanted to lick away each drop, to taste the warm saltiness of his skin. She must have made some sound, because his hands tightened, hurting her, and for a moment his face was open and she thought she read desire in his eyes, but almost instantly it was gone and he laughed and said, 'Let's get him, shall we?' and she found herself being pulled into chasing Steve and trying to duck him.

After about an hour they went back to the hotel and sat around in loungers, sunbathing until the sun went down, drinking, smoking and talking desultorily. The two men seemed to know each other quite well, they were at ease with one another and had 'in' jokes that meant nothing to Cordelia. It seemed that they had arrived in Sri Lanka more or less at the same time, Steve having signed a two-year contract with the dam construction company. Intellectually they were probably very different; Steve was a far more practical type than Marcus, a man of action who was used to giving orders and being responsible for the people under him. He was gregarious, an extrovert, whereas Marcus was more of a loner, happy to share the company of others but needing often to be quite private and alone, and never finding his own company boring. He was well read too, understandably, which Steve wasn't, and Marcus was capable of taking a conversation to far greater depths than the younger man could.

The hotel provided changing rooms for visitors, so Cordelia was able to shower the sea salt and sun oil from her skin and change into a dress she had brought with her. It was pale yellow with a halter neck, no back at all and a full, pleated skirt. It looked good against her tan. Her hair, too, when she had dried it with the blow-dryer provided by the hotel, gleamed a lighter gold from the sun. She looked golden all over; her dress, the honey gold of her skin, her hair; she even had gold sandals for her feet.

The men were waiting for her when she came out. As she walked down the corridor they both looked her over, the way a man does look at a woman, speculatively, his eyes going down over her body. Steve's gaze became frankly admiring, but she couldn't read Marcus's face, he had the ability to completely hide his feelings. She walked between them into the dining-room and every head in the place seemed to turn in their direction as they were shown to their table. The glances of the women were frankly envious as they saw her with the two tall, good-looking men, and those of the men weren't exactly unappreciative either, which gave Cordelia a much-needed boost to her ego.

Their table became a centre of laughter and gaiety; Cordelia putting herself out to sparkle and amuse. Steve lapped it up, obviously enjoying himself hugely, and Marcus, too, joined in and appeared to be getting a kick out of the evening. Whether he was acting a part, Cordelia wasn't at all sure, but once or twice she caught him looking at her with an abstracted frown in his eyes. And she was definitely putting on an act, giving everything to it like a star hoping to win an Oscar. She drank quite a bit, too, but didn't even feel lightheaded.

After dinner they went into the night club attached to the hotel and drank cocktails based on arrack, a locally made spirit very similar to whisky. A local group played their version of the European hit numbers, much too loud, of course, but then all discos everywhere were much too loud, after a while you gave up trying to talk and just let the music wash over you, the beat get into your bones. There were other European women there, nearly all married and with their men, just here and there an odd girl watched over anxiously by her parents or two girls together who were soon dancing with some European men who were also on their own. Cordelia peered round in the comparative gloom looking for the Sri Lankan women, but the only ones who looked dark enough to be natives wore European dress and stayed close to the sides of the men they were with. There were plenty of young native men there, though; all impossibly slim and neatly dressed, and obviously on the prowl, looking for European girls to dance with. One came up and asked Cordelia almost before she'd walked into the place, but she didn't have to say no, both Steve and Marcus said it for her.

They guarded her like two dogs guarding a sheep—even more fiercely than the parents with their daughters, Cordelia thought wryly. But Steve explained in a lull in the music, 'Sri Lankan men and women don't dance together like we do; they think it's more or less promiscuous. But the men have seen it on the American television programmes and they go to all the night clubs hoping to get a dance. It really turns them on. If they can't get a girl they even dance with each other.'

When the music began again Steve asked her to dance. It would have to be Steve, of course, and not Marcus, but she smiled and went with him on to the small dance floor bathed in swirling, alternating bands of coloured lights so that the dancers had an eerie, ghostlike look. Cordelia immediately became aware of all the eyes on her, watching her every move. She wished now that she hadn't worn such a skimpy dress, had worn one with a back, with long sleeves even! She tried to lose herself, to forget everything except the music, but it was impossible; she wanted to keep turning her head to look at Marcus, to see if his eyes were among those that watched her. The dance came to an end at last and they went back to their seats. 'That was great,' Steve told her, his hand on her waist. 'I haven't enjoyed dancing so much since I've been over here.'

Cordelia managed to give him a smile of thanks, but she eagerly sat down again, hoping that Marcus would ask her next time. But he didn't seem in any hurry to do so and they sat and sipped their cocktails, using the swizzle sticks to search through the fruit and ice to find the liquid underneath. Another, extremely brave, Sri Lankan youth asked her to dance and didn't want to take no for an answer, then Steve stood up to his full height and glared at him and the poor young man melted away.

The band changed to a slower beat and Marcus touched her arm. 'Cordelia?'

She didn't look at him, just gave a small nod and walked ahead of him on to the floor. He put his arm round her and took hold of her right hand, lightly, not holding her close. Cordelia's head came about level with his shoulder, but she didn't raise it to look at him; she kept her eyes fixed on the collar of the silk shirt he was wearing where it opened to reveal the dark column of his neck. They danced slowly round the little floor. Occasionally someone brushed against her, but Cordelia wasn't aware of it, all she could feel was the touch of his hands, his closeness—and yet he was so very far away. She was very tense, her nerves felt as if they could snap at any moment. She wanted to be held close in his arms as she had been last night, to feel the warmth and strength of his embrace. Her hand trembled and she felt Marcus stiffen. Slowly she raised her head to look into his eyes. For a moment they were vulnerable and she could see the tension in his own face, then he had himself under control again and gave her a casual smile. But it was between them now, like a live thing, this emotion that he wouldn't allow to show, this desire that he had squashed before it could take fire. Neither of them spoke, the atmosphere between them was suddenly so charged that a word could have acted like a fuse. They danced on, but there might just have been the two of them in the room, so unaware was Cordelia of the people around them. She searched his face for some sign, some acknowledgment, but he wouldn't meet her eyes, again—like this morning—keeping his face as expressionless as a mask.

When they sat down again, Cordelia turned her attention to Steve, asking him questions about himself while the band took a break, and getting up to dance with him without hesitation when they came back. She danced with Steve the rest of the evening, they hardly left the floor except to take a drink. Marcus sat alone at the table watching them, a brooding look about his mouth, making no attempt to ask any other girl in the room to dance. At eleven-thirty he stood up rather abruptly and said, 'We'd better be heading back.'

'But it's early yet,' Steve protested.

'We've a long drive ahead of us, remember?' Marcus pointed out.

Steve looked to Cordelia to back him up, but she only said, 'I'll get my things,' so he was disappointed.

When they went out to the car she was worried that Steve might try to sit in the back with her, so she quickly yawned and said, 'I'm tired. Would you mind if I sit in the back instead of you, Steve, so that I can stretch out?'

He had to agree, of course; it would have been ill-mannered and obvious to have done otherwise.

It was a very fine night, the stars were out and looked like sparkling jewels against the warm, dark velvet of the sky. Strange stars, in constellations she didn't recognise. Cordelia lay across the back seat and watched them as they drove along. The two men were talking, the sound of their voices rolled over her, but she wasn't listening. If they had been talking about her, she might have done, but she knew they wouldn't do that. She could see the profile of Marcus's head as he concentrated on the road, outlined by the faint glow thrown up by the dashboard lights. What was he thinking? Cordelia wondered. Did he care about her at all? She would have given everything she had to know. But apart from that one moment when they had been dancing, he was like a closed book to her, she had no idea whatsoever of his true feelings, or even whether he had any for her at all. The car bounced gently along the rutted roads, for once quiet now, and Cordelia wearily closed her eyes, the motion rocking her into sleep.

She didn't waken until the car stopped and the lack of movement penetrated to her subconscious. Opening her eyes, she found that she was lying in a long bar of moonlight and that both men were looking over the backs of their seats at her.

'You're home,' Steve told her, adding with a clumsy attempt at gallantry, 'You look like the Sleeping Beauty lying there.'

Cordelia smiled and sat up, pushing her hair back from her head. 'So which one of you is going to kiss me and turn into a handsome prince?' she quipped lightly.

Marcus grinned. 'Are you saying that we're a couple of frogs?'

'We-l-l . . .' She raised her eyebrows expressively.

He laughed and got out of the car, opened the rear door and helped her out. After having been curled up in the back of the car for so long, Cordelia's legs felt rather stiff and it was a moment or two before she followed the men over to Steve's car. Steve had been saying something to Marcus in a low voice, but he broke off when she came over.

'You sure you won't stay the night?' Marcus said to him. 'You can doss down on the settee.'

'Thanks, but I've got to get back.'

'Goodnight, then.'

They shook hands and Marcus turned and walked towards the house. Cordelia, too, offered her hand. 'Goodnight, Steve. Nice meeting you.' She half-turned to follow Marcus, but Steve kept hold of her hand. Reluctantly she turned back to him, more or less knowing what was coming.

'Don't go in for a minute,' Steve said. 'I'd like to talk to you.'

'I'm tired, Steve. It's very late.' Cordelia glanced over her shoulder, looking to see if Marcus was waiting for her, but he had already gone into the house. Immediately she felt a stab of anger, guessing that Steve had asked him to leave them alone together.

'It won't take a minute. Look, I've really enjoyed tonight. I thought we might go out some other evening.'

'Yes, of course,' Cordelia agreed lightly. 'Whenever you and Marcus are both free.' She tried to pull her hand away, but he hung on.

'That wasn't what I meant; I meant just the two of us. In fact,' he went on with a rush, 'I've got a week's leave owing to me and I thought perhaps I could take you around the island. There are some places I haven't seen myself yet, like Adam's Peak, and we could do them together.'

'Thanks, but I really don't want to tie myself down. And besides, I promised to help Marcus with his book in return for his hospitality.'

'He won't hold you to that.'

'I know, which is precisely why I intend to keep my promise. He's been very kind to us, Steve. The least I can do is to help him in any way I can.'

He put his other hand on her waist and tried to draw her towards him. 'But I want to see you again, very much,' he told her thickly.

Cordelia held herself stiffly, not wanting him to kiss her. 'Look, I enjoyed tonight, it was fun, but I've only just met you . . .'

'Is there someone back in England? Is that what you're trying to say?'

'No,' Cordelia admitted. 'No one special. But that doesn't mean that I want to commit myself to—well, to being tied down. And anyway, you know about my father; he may want to leave here and go to a hospital as soon as he's well enough to be moved. I'm sorry, Steve, but . . .'

'All right, you don't have to go on; I get the message. I thought we hit it off okay,' he added ruefully.

'We did, and I like you. But I just don't want to get involved. Right?'

'Right. But if I phone or come over will you come out with me if you're free?'

With a little sigh, Cordelia nodded. 'But only as long as I'm free to say no if I can't.'

'Or don't want to.'

'That, too,' she agreed coolly.

Steve grinned suddenly. 'You're very determined, aren't you?'

'I like to be independent,' she corrected him. Pulling herself free of his arms, she said, 'Goodnight, Steve. Drive back safely.'

He didn't move immediately but watched her as she walked to the bungalow. At the door she turned and nodded to him. He lifted a hand in salute and climbed into his car. Marcus had already gone to his room; Cordelia went quietly to her own and listened to the noise of Steve's engine as the sound echoed through the quiet hills.

CHAPTER SIX

SUGIN came back the next day. Cordelia didn't sleep very well and got up early, looking forward eagerly to having breakfast with Marcus, but when she went out on to the verandah Sugin was standing by his chair, her arm along the back of it in a familiar gesture. Cordelia met the rather malicious look in the other girl's eyes and quickly looked away. 'Good morning, Marcus. Hallo, Sugin. How's your sister?' Somehow she forced herself to sound natural.

'She is much better now. How is your father?' The returned politeness mocked back at her.

'Coming along famously, thank you.' She sat down and poured herself some fruit juice, hoping that Sugin would go away, but of course she didn't. Smiling at Marcus, Cordelia queried, 'Work today?'

'Unless you'd rather take the car and go sightseeing.'

'You should go to Aukana,' Sugin put in. 'There is a statue of the Buddha there that you should see.'

'Thank you, but I've already seen the replica in Colombo, and I think I've had quite enough of doing the tourist bit for a while. I could do with a few quiet days,' Cordelia said firmly.

If Marcus noticed the battle between them he didn't show it. 'Good. I'd like to get on today.' He talked to both girls impartially until they had finished breakfast and then stood up immediately. 'Let's make a start before it gets too hot.'

122

Dr Matara came during the morning and said that her father was well enough to sit out on the verandah for a while each day. He also dispensed with the day nurse's visits, saying that Marcus's servants were quite able to see to the patient's needs now, but he went over her father's different medicines with Cordelia, making her responsible for seeing that he took them correctly. They took a break for lunch, but Cordelia said she wasn't hungry, instead putting on her bikini and finding a secluded patch of the garden where she sunbathed until it was time to get back to work.

Marcus was much the same as he had been before their trip to Sigiriya; friendly, willing to converse intelligently on any subject she chose, he even flirted with her a little once or twice, but he made no attempt to kiss her again and there was nothing behind it; he made sure she knew that.

After dinner they both went in to see James Allingham, but after a while the two men began to play chess. Cordelia tried to read a book but couldn't settle to it, so she excused herself and went for a walk in the garden, somehow feeling that neither man was sorry to see her go. Any faint hope she might have had of Marcus joining her died when she saw Sugin still in the house, her small, curvaceous figure outlined by the electric lights as she moved from room to room shutting the windows.

The next day passed very similarly except that Steve phoned in the early evening, before dinner. Cordelia was in her room and quickly slipped on a bathrobe over her underwear when Marcus knocked on her door. 'Steve's on the line,' he told her. 'Wants to know if you'd care to spend the evening up at the Expatriates Club.'

'Will you be going?'

He shook his head. 'I've promised to give your father a chance to get his revenge at chess.'

'Then I won't go either, thanks.'

'Why not, Steve will take care of you?'

'No. I don't want to go alone.'

A shadow crossed Marcus's face and he kept his eyes fixed on hers, as if willing himself not to let his eyes wander down to where her robe had slipped open a little and revealed the white valley between her breasts. 'How would you like it if we all went there tomorrow evening, then?'

Cordelia nodded and said a little huskily, 'Yes, I'd like that.'

'Okay, I'll tell Steve.'

When Marcus had said that they would all go to the Club, Cordelia had thought that meant him, Steve and herself; she hadn't realised that it also included Sugin. She went eagerly out to join him, looking forward to being alone with him on the journey to the dam site—and even more to the return journey home, but all her hopes fell ludicrously when she saw the Sri Lankan girl, dressed in a blue spangled sari, waiting in the hallway.

Trying desperately not to let her disappointment show, Cordelia smiled brightly and followed them out to the car. At least she got to sit in the front seat beside him, although Sugin's presence in the back, as quiet as Steve's had been talkative, was just as inhibiting. The drive to the dam site took about half an hour, but it was dark before they set off, so there was nothing to see. At this time of night the roads were still busy with people going home from work in the plantations and Marcus had to drive carefully, dodging the unlit bicycles and the transport lorries from the tea factories, loaded down with the people who were packed in far more closely than any cattle truck would be in Britain; at home, Cordelia reflected, if animals had been discovered packed in that tightly it would have made newspaper headlines and the whole country would have been up in arms!

They got to the Expatriates Club about eight-thirty and Steve was waiting to meet them. He immediately appropriated Cordelia for himself, taking her arm and drawing her into a big room where there was a bar along the whole length of the narrower wall and a largish space set aside as a dance floor. Tables were set out around the rest of the room and most of them were occupied. There seemed to be a majority of men in the room, all European in appearance, and Cordelia was surprised to see quite a few white women as well as several Sri Lankan girls.

At the moment when Steve escorted her into the room, there happened to be a lull in the music coming from a disco-type set-up over in the corner. They paused for a moment in the doorway, waiting for Marcus and Sugin, and all eyes seemed to turn towards them. Immediately Steve was the object of all sorts of comments, from the outrightly ribald to the plainly envious. It was obviously the sort of club where all the men knew each other so well they could be rude to one another without giving offence. Steve merely grinned goodnaturedly and led them across to an empty table. Cordelia sat down and found herself opposite Sugin, so she immediately turned and began to talk brightly to Steve.

As soon as the music started, Steve took her on the floor, introducing her to several of his friends as they danced. It turned out that many of the men she had taken to be European were in fact Australian, with one or two Americans among them. The white women were nearly all wives who had accompanied their husbands and who lived in small houses provided by the dam company, or girl-friends who were over on visits. None of the women were without a more or less permanent man, which made Cordelia the only really unattached white girl there. Steve of course made it known that he had first claim, as it were, but that didn't stop most of the other single men who hadn't got girls from coming over to be introduced. So Cordelia found herself greatly in demand and danced more or less non-stop. She was glad of it, not wanting to have to sit and look at Sugin's face all evening, a face that grew more disdainful as Cordelia let her hair down and really got into the beat. But Cordelia didn't care; she was enjoying herself despite Sugin's disapproval and Marcus's withdrawn coolness. He was sitting back in his chair, watching her rather broodingly as he drew on his cigarette. He didn't ask her to dance, but then he didn't ask Sugin either, no one did, although some of the other Sri Lankan girls were attempting to dance Western style, even though not very successfully.

There was a contrariness about Cordelia tonight. She looked at Marcus's dark features and thought, damn him, why the hell should I care about him? The man doesn't even know his own mind! She turned a laughing face up to the man she was dancing with and let him take her back to his table afterwards to meet some of his friends. She stayed chatting to them for about ten minutes, then Steve came over to claim her.

Later, after a particularly strenuous dance, Cordelia laughingly insisted on having a rest for a while. 'I'm exhausted,' she complained. 'I don't know whether it's the height, the humidity or the heat, but it really takes it out of you, dancing here.' She took a long pull at her drink and looked at Sugin. Rather recklessly she said, 'I notice you don't dance, Sugin. Don't you know how?'

The other girl's nose curled. 'Anyone can throw themselves about like that. That is not dancing. Real dancing is very graceful and has to be learned from a small child. Each dance is traditional and all the movements have to be learned. Throwing yourself about like a mad woman is not dancing.'

Marcus went to say something, but Cordelia broke in hotly, 'What you describe is professional dancing. In Britain we have a great deal of professional dancing—the ballet, for instance, which is far more traditional and graceful than your dancing; you have to be really good to dance in the ballet. But what I'm talking about is dancing by ordinary people for enjoyment. Do you know how to do that? Or do you only do it for money?' Cordelia added bitchily.

'Respectable girls would not dance so with a man,' Sugin retorted with equal venom.

'But we're not talking about respectable girls— we're talking about you,' Cordelia answered sweetly.

Marcus got to his feet, an angry frown between his eyes. Taking hold of Cordelia's arm, he pulled her to her feet and led her on to the dance floor. 'Why the hell are you picking on Sugin?' he demanded.

Cordelia bit her lip, realising how petty it must seem to him, but she couldn't tell him how blatantly the other girl had tried to get rid of her. 'She doesn't like me,' she answered weakly.

'So what? You have every advantage that she doesn't.'

No, not every one, Cordelia thought miserably. She has you and I don't.

'And you know she can't get up and dance,' Marcus was going on. 'It's against their custom.'

'There are other Sri Lankan girls here dancing,' Cordelia said defensively. 'And there were quite a few men in that night club in Colombo.'

'These girls are a lower class than Sugin. And even then they wouldn't do it if there were any of their own men around.'

'I'm surprised Sugin lowered herself to come here at all if she's so high class,' Cordelia couldn't resist remarking waspishly.

Marcus's frown deepened. 'She came because I asked her to.'

He didn't explain why, which left Cordelia to wonder miserably if it had been because he didn't want to be alone with her during the drive, or just because he preferred Sugin's company to hers. And neither reason was very flattering.

The dance was a slow one and seemed to go on for ages. She wished it was over. For the first time Cordelia didn't want to be near him; she knew that from his point of view she deserved his anger, and the fact that it was in some way justified didn't make her feel any better. She felt wretched and just wanted to go home. But 'home' was the bungalow where she would have to see both of them together, knowing that they were lovers. She longed suddenly to get right away, to never see Marcus again. To go back to England and forget that she'd ever met him, forget that one night when he had taken her into the garden and kissed and caressed her—that one perfect night. She quivered and gave a half-sob.

Marcus's arm tightened round her waist. 'What is it?'

'Nothing.' She kept her head down.

'Cordelia?' When she did nothing he ordered, 'Cordelia, look at me.'

Slowly she raised her head, her eyes dark and vulnerable. Her lips trembled as she tried to control herself. Marcus's eyes met hers, searched her face. His lips moved and she thought he murmured something under his breath, but it was too low for her to hear. Turning her head away, she said stiltedly, 'I'm tired. Can we go home soon?'

'Yes, of course. Now, if you like.'

They went back to their table and he said to the others, 'Time for us to go, I think. Thanks for a great evening, Steve.'

'But you're not going yet! It's still early. Stay for a bit longer,' Steve protested.

'The girls are tired.'

'Cordelia isn't. Look, you take Sugin home now if she wants to go and I'll drive Cordelia home later.'

'Oh, no, that's far too much trouble,' Cordelia protested quickly. 'Thanks, Steve, but I'll go home with the others.'

'It's no trouble, I can easily . . .'

'Steve, I'd rather,' Cordelia told him sharply, her voice rising.

Catching the slightly hysterical note, Steve looked at her face and saw the strain in it. 'Okay. I'll see you off.' He walked with them to the car, hanging back so that he and Cordelia were behind the other two. 'Can I call you in a couple of days?'

Cordelia immediately felt remorseful for having snapped at him and nodded. 'Yes, that will be fine. Thanks for tonight, Steve.' She touched his hand in farewell, but Steve caught hold of her arm so that she had to stop. Turning her round to face him, he gave her a light kiss on the mouth. 'See you, then.'

'Yes. See you.' Cordelia went over to the car. Sugin was already sitting in the front seat and Marcus was standing at the back, holding the door open for her. Cordelia didn't know whether or not he had seen Steve kiss her; it wouldn't have mattered if he had, it was only a peck, but even so she was glad of the darkness that hid the flush that came to her cheeks.

It was Sugin's turn to become animated on the way home; she talked exclusively to Marcus, of people and places that Cordelia knew nothing about, shutting her out completely. When they got to the bungalow Cordelia said a hurried goodnight and went straight to her room, turning the handbasin taps full on so that she wouldn't hear them both going into Marcus's bedroom.

James Allingham was rather surprised at her solicitousness the next day. Cordelia went to his room first thing to give him his medicines and encouraged him to let the houseboy dress him after breakfast so that he could go and sit on the verandah before the sun got too hot. 'You're doing fine,' she encouraged him. 'You'll soon be fit enough to take a walk in the garden.' And then, she added to herself, you'll be well enough to take a car ride to the nearest hotel. Because all she wanted now was to get away from Marcus as soon as possible.

She worked nearly all that day. Marcus was

with her in the workroom for some of the time,
but when her father came out on to the verandah
he went to sit with him, leaving Cordelia to get on
on her own. She typed very fast, wanting to get the
job done with so that it wouldn't be on her
conscience when she left. By the time she had
finished that day the pile of beautifully clean typed
manuscript had grown considerably and she was
only a couple of chapters behind Marcus's
rewritten and corrected draft.

Standing up, Cordelia stretched her shoulders,
her back aching. The sun had started to set and
she hadn't even noticed. Marcus came in while she
was putting the cover on the typewriter and looked
at the pile of typed sheets. 'You've done a lot
today. You've almost caught me up.' She nodded
and went to turn away, but he put his hands on
her shoulders. 'You don't have to work so hard,
you know.'

Lightly she answered, 'I don't like to be behind.
Would you excuse me?' She tried to step to one
side. 'It must be time to change for dinner.'

Marcus let her pass. 'Going out with Steve
tonight?'

'No.'

'You seem to get on with him all right.'

Cordelia shrugged, her back to him. 'He's nice
enough.'

'Well, don't feel that you have to stay here and
help me if he asks you out.'

Biting her lip hard, Cordelia managed, 'No, I
won't. Of course not,' then quickly escaped to her
own room.

Seeing to her father's medicines and general
wellbeing helped to take her mind off other things,
and she also went to sit with him for a while in the

evening. Marcus came too and the two men again played chess. Cordelia sat in a chair with her legs curled up under her, a book in her hands, but quite often her attention drifted from the pages and she sat gazing broodingly at first Marcus, then her father. After a couple of hours, Marcus went to get some drinks and James Allingham looked at her from under drawn brows. 'Is something the matter?'

Cordelia raised her head in surprise. 'What do you mean?'

'You've been watching the pair of us instead of reading nearly all evening. If there's something on your mind you'd better tell me.'

'It's nothing really, only . . .' she hesitated, 'only I think it would be a good idea if we moved into a hotel as soon as you're well enough to make the journey.'

Her father frowned. 'Has Marcus said he wants us to go?' he demanded bluntly.

'Oh, no, nothing like that. It's just that—well, I think it would be a good idea, that's all,' Cordelia said lamely.

'I suppose you're bored,' he said rather peevishly. 'Well, I'm very comfortable, and I'm being looked after far better than I would be in any hotel. If you don't like it here you can always go somewhere by yourself; I'm sure Marcus wouldn't object—although I thought you were supposed to be helping him with his book. I suppose you don't like having to work, is that it?'

'Not at all,' Cordelia answered coldly. 'I offered to help him and I shall continue to do so until it's finished. I don't want to take advantage of his hospitality any longer than necessary, that's all.

After all,' she added tartly, 'he didn't exactly invite us here, did he?'

Whatever answer her father had been going to make was stifled as Marcus came back into the room. They started a new game, and Cordelia very soon said goodnight and went to bed.

By lunchtime the next day she had caught Marcus up on the book. He sat quietly at his desk, absorbed in his work and didn't notice that she'd stopped typing. She whiled away half an hour by giving the typewriter a much-needed clean, then went to persuade her father to join them on the verandah for lunch. She fussed around him unnecessarily, making sure that he was sitting fully in the shade, and also between Marcus and herself. He muttered once or twice about fussy women, but Cordelia noticed that he took full advantage of everything she did for him.

After lunch she changed into her bikini and went to sunbathe in the garden again. She chose a secluded place among the spice trees where the sun beat down on a clear patch of grass and slipped out of her sundress to lie down on the big, gaily-coloured beach towel she had brought with her. For an hour or so she did her back, feeling the sun soaking into her skin, then rolled over to do her front. The sun beat down on to her and she closed her eyes against the glare, but still it seemed to scorch through her lids. Vaguely she told herself that she ought to put on some more oil now that she'd turned over, but she felt too lazy and apathetic to do so. She let her mind go blank, wandering wherever it cared to take her, not thinking of anyone in particular, although it somehow seemed always to come back to Marcus. She dozed and woke, dozed again. The next time she opened her eyes Marcus was standing over her. At first he didn't notice she was awake because his eyes were on her body, slowly travelling its length, savouring its slim, taut beauty, examining her her as he would never have done ordinarily. Then his eyes reached her face and he saw her staring back at him. Their eyes met and held for a moment that seemed to stretch into eternity. His eyes, his face, were for that moment her whole world and nothing on earth would have made her break the spell. But presently Marcus's eyebrows flickered and he dropped to his knees beside her.

'You'll burn up if you don't put some of this on,' he told her, picking up the bottle of oil, his voice harsh, unnatural. Unscrewing the bottle, he poured some of the rich amber liquid into his hand and began to rub it into her shoulders, then down her body.

Cordelia wanted to close her eyes, to let sensuality take over as she savoured each stroke of his hands, but instead she kept them open, fixed on his face. His hands moved slowly, rhythmically, around the edge of her strapless bikini top, down each bone of her ribs and the inward curve of her waist. He didn't look at her face, just watched his hands working on her body, the oil turning the light down of fine hairs on her skin into spun silk. He seemed fascinated by what he was doing, his thumbs slowly outlining her hipbones, his finger-tips feathering along just under the edge of her bikini. Cordelia gasped, unable to withstand the sensations he was arousing in her any longer.

His hands stilled as he at last turned to look at her face. She gazed back at him, lips parted sensuously, the need to be loved large in her eyes.

But even though her eyes searched his face so intently, she couldn't tell his thoughts or his feelings, as always he kept them hidden behind enigmatic features. Huskily, on a note of heartfelt pleading, she said, 'Don't do this to me.'

His hands, that were still resting on her hips, moved involuntarily, tightening for a brief instant. Then he leant back on his heels and got to his feet in one swift, agile movement. 'Sorry,' he said laconically. 'But you need protection from the sun here.' Giving her a brief nod, he strode away through the trees.

Cordelia sat up and watched him go, thinking bitterly that she needed protection from him, not the sun. He had chosen to interpret her words as telling him to stop oiling her, but both of them knew that she had meant far more than that. Automatically she picked up the bottle of oil and finished off her legs, her hands unsteady. A pulse beat in her throat and she felt incredibly hot, but hot from the inside, not from the sun. Lightly she ran her hands over herself, remembering how *his* hands had felt, wishing now that she had let him go on, but part of her also fiercely glad that she had sent him away. She wanted now, more than ever, to get away from him. If he touched her again she didn't think that she would be able to bear it; she would do something crazy like taking the first plane back to England—or else telling Marcus that she loved him and wanted to go to bed with him. Either of which actions would lead to unbearable consequences. Which was why, when Steve phoned her an hour or so later and asked her to have dinner with him that evening, she accepted without the slightest hesitation.

They had dinner at the Hill Club in Nuwara

Eliya, the same place that Cordelia had visited
with her father just before the accident. Steve
called for her at seven, looking smart and different
in a suit and tie, and looked at her feminine, lacy
dress in admiring approval. 'You look beautiful,'
he told her a little awkwardly, as if he wasn't
accustomed to paying such lavish compliments.
Cordelia smiled and thanked him, able to
appreciate his approbation even if it did come
from the wrong man. He was rather disappointed
to find that she had been there before as he had
wanted to surprise her, but Cordelia was as sweet
about it as she knew how and she soon had him
laughing and happy again.

He was an interesting man to have a date with,
he had travelled a lot and had a store of good
stories and anecdotes to tell. Ordinarily she would
have enjoyed being with him, but more than once
she found her mind wandering back to the
bungalow and its occupants. Was Marcus playing
chess with her father again tonight? Or was he
devoting the evening to Sugin?

'So what do you think he said?'

Steve's question brought her back with a jerk
and she managed to smile and shake her head.
'I've no idea. What did he say?'

'He said he found the panties hanging on a peg
in the men's changing rooms at the rugby club!'

This was obviously the punch line of a funny
story, and Cordelia wished she'd heard the
beginning; it sounded intriguing.

They ate a beautifully cooked and served meal in
the dining-room and afterwards danced to the music
of a trio of Sri Lankans who played all the old
American swing and jazz numbers of the thirties and
forties; Glenn Miller and other big band tunes.

Music that sounded incongruous in that place and played by those people, and a far cry from the disco at the Expatriates Club, although Cordelia enjoyed it just as much, if not more, or at least would have done if Marcus had been there. Vainly she tried to push him out of her mind, to concentrate on Steve—after all, he was the one who was trying to give her a good time. But however much she tried to be nice to him, her heart just wasn't in it. He tried to draw her close as they danced and she smiled and allowed him to do so, but after a few minutes she moved away again, not deliberately, just from a natural reluctance to be held so closely by a man she didn't want. He tried to encourage her to talk about herself, but she told him only a little and then changed the subject, unwilling to give anything of herself to him except her company.

It was almost one in the morning before they left and Steve drove her back to the bungalow. 'How about coming sightseeing with me?' he asked her as they drew up outside. 'Will you be able to make it some time?'

'Yes, I can come tomorrow, if you like?'

Steve looked surprised and pleased. 'You mean later today tomorrow?'

Cordelia laughed. 'Yes. If you can get the time off from the dam.'

'That's no problem. I told you, they owe me some leave. Where would you like to go?'

'You choose.' She stifled a yawn. 'You know the places I've seen, so I'll leave it to you.'

'Okay. What time shall I pick you up? Would eight-thirty be too early?'

'No, that will be fine.' She put a hand on the door handle. 'I'd better say goodnight, then, so that you can get back and get some sleep.'

'In a minute.' Steve reached out and put a hand on either side of her shoulders, drew her back towards him. 'It's been great tonight, Cordelia. You're a wonderful girl.'

'Thanks, Steve, but I . . .'

Her words were cut off as he kissed her. She didn't stop him, and discovered that he'd been around quite a bit as far as that was concerned too. After five minutes or so, when he became more passionate and his hands started to wander, Cordelia drew back and said firmly, 'I'm going in now. I'll see you in the morning.' And she got out of the car at once, leaving him no chance of stopping her.

The house was very quiet as she turned the lights off behind her and went to her room. She undressed quickly, then remembered that she was meeting Steve at eight-thirty and that she hadn't got an alarm clock. The best thing to do, she decided, was to write a note asking to be called at seven-thirty and for breakfast at eight, and leave it where the houseboy would find it in the morning. Quickly she wrote the note, and then, confident that everyone in the house was asleep, walked out as she was, in pale blue shortie pyjamas, her face unmade-up, her hair brushed loose and swinging free about her head, to prop the note up in a prominent place where it was sure to be seen.

Not bothering to turn on the lights, she stuck her note on the handle of the kitchen door, but as she was coming back through the sitting-room, the door of the study suddenly opened and Marcus stood framed in the light shining through the doorway. 'Who's there?' he demanded sharply.

For a moment, Cordelia had a childish desire to bolt back to her room, but managed to overcome it and stay where she was, although her heart had immediately begun to race. 'It—it's me,' she managed. 'I'm sorry if I disturbed you.'

Marcus moved further into the room but didn't bother to switch on the light. 'Is something the matter?'

'No. I was just leaving a note for your houseboy to give me an early call in the morning.'

'You're going out with Steve again tomorrow?'

'Yes.'

'So you had a good time tonight?'

'It was all right.' It felt odd to be talking together like this in semi-darkness, the house silent around them. And the conversation was quite meaningless, just words; Cordelia was hardly aware of them. Her eyes were fixed on Marcus, standing tall and shadowed, his shirt open to reveal the long column of his throat, his sleeves rolled up above his elbows. Moving a little nearer, he said, 'Where did you go?'

'The Hill Club at Nuwara Eliya.'

Silence fell between them, a silence loud with the sparks of electricity that their physical need for each other generated. Then Marcus broke the silence by saying thickly, 'You look about fourteen years old, like that.'

'Do I? But I'm not.' Deliberately she moved a few steps so that the light from the study outlined her body through the thin material of her pyjamas. 'Am I?' she whispered.

'No.' The word seemed to be dragged out of him and he thrust his hands into his pockets as if he couldn't control them.

'Aren't you going to kiss me goodnight?' Cordelia asked huskily.

He stared at her for a long moment, then

answered by saying, 'I don't think that would be a very good idea.'

'Why not? You were willing enough to kiss me the other night in the garden,' she reminded him, an edge of hurt in her voice.

'Yes, I know. But maybe that wasn't such a good idea, either.'

Cordelia's eyes grew wide in her suddenly set face. 'What are you saying?' she demanded harshly. 'That you didn't enjoy what we did?'

'Oh, yes, I enjoyed it,' Marcus muttered, half to himself. 'Maybe I enjoyed it too much.' Seeing her distress, he moved closer and at last took his hands from his pockets and put them on her bare arms. Immediately a kind of electric shock ran through her and she quivered with emotion. 'That night—I think we both got more than we bargained for.'

'Is that—so wrong?' Cordelia gazed up at him, wanting to touch him, but afraid.

'For us—yes,' he told her, his voice suddenly becoming harsh.

Cordelia winced as if he'd struck her. 'But why? I don't understand. Don't you—don't you want me?' she asked desperately, her voice breaking.

'Want you?' His hands tightened and he said something under his breath, something that sounded like a curse. 'That has nothing to do with it,' he told her shortly.

'Doesn't it? I should have thought it had everything to do with it.' Throwing pride to the winds, she said, 'I know that I want you, Marcus. Want you very much.'

'Don't say that.' He took a step away from her. 'You're too young to . . .'

'Oh, for heaven's sake! I'm nearly twenty-one

years old. How old do you think one has to be to fall in love?'

He grew suddenly still and stared at her. 'Are you saying that you're in love with me?'

Slowly, her voice choking with emotion, Cordelia answered, 'Yes. Yes, I rather think I am.'

For a long moment he didn't move, didn't speak, while she waited in agony to see what he would do. Then, his voice harsh, grating, he said, 'Really? Or is it my job that you're in love with? The fact that there's some glamour and fame attached to me? Do you really think you'd have fallen for me so quickly if I hadn't been a writer?'

Cordelia gaped at him in stunned astonishment. 'But—but your job has nothing to do with the way I feel. It wouldn't matter what you did for a living, I'd still . . .'

'No? Have you even bothered to think about it?' He swung away from her, took a few paces across the room and gripped the back of a chair, his knuckles showing white. 'Okay, maybe you really believe that what you feel is love. But this isn't the first time this has happened to me, Cordelia. Young girls tend to fall for men in what they think are glamour jobs: actors, writers, racing drivers, pilots.' He smiled rather sardonically at bracketing himself with the last two. 'Then either the glamour wears off or else the man goes on to another girl. It's very nice for the men who take advantage of it, of course,' he added cynically.

'And have you—taken advantage of it?' Cordelia couldn't help asking.

'On occasion,' he admitted.

'But you don't feel like doing so on this—occasion?'

He turned abruptly. 'You're a guest in my house.'

She stared at him, anger mounting inside. 'So why didn't you think of that before you started—*flirting* with me?'

'Because I didn't expect things to get out of hand—or so quickly. I forgot that you were too young to know how to play that kind of game.'

'A game? Is that all it is to you? Oh, for God's sake!' She threw her arms wide in exasperation. 'What do you think I am—some infatuated teenager? I'm not, Marcus. I swear I'm not. What I feel for you is very real. Please believe me.'

His mouth thinned into a sceptical, mirthless smile. 'Isn't it time you got some sleep? *You don't want to keep Steve waiting in the morning, do you?*'

Cordelia gazed at him, her vision gradually blurred by tears, then she gave a helpless sob and ran to her room.

She was on time to meet Steve, for the simple reason that she had hardly slept all night. When he drove up she was already waiting by the front porch, a picnic hamper at her feet and sunglasses hiding the dark shadows around her eyes.

'Hi!' she greeted him brightly. 'I talked the cook into giving us a picnic lunch. Don't bother to get out. Here.' She handed him the hamper to stow in the back and climbed in beside him. 'How are you this morning?'

'Fine. And you?'

'Oh, great, just great. And raring to go. Where *are* we going, by the way?' she added as he reversed and then drove back down the driveway.

'I thought we'd go to Polonnaruwa. It's the other big ancient city. That's if it's okay with you,' he added anxiously.

'Sounds fine. Have you been there before?'

'No, it will be the first time for me too.'

Cordelia kept up an animated conversation nearly all the way so that she wouldn't have time to remember last night. She never wanted to think about the humiliation she had felt then as long as she lived.

The city with the unpronounceable name was nearer than the one she had visited with Marcus driving as a guide, so they had more time to spend there, but although Cordelia kept up the act of being interested in everything she saw, she soon came to the conclusion that one ancient city was very much like another. By midday they were both flagging and Steve suggested having their picnic under a tree, but this reminded Cordelia too vividly of a similar occasion with Marcus, so she firmly insisted that they go to a hotel where they ate their picnic sitting decorously at a table near the swimming pool while drinking cold beer from the hotel's bar.

Steve had a pair of trunks in the car, so he swam first to cool off while Cordelia leant back in a lounger and watched him. He stripped off very well, his body muscular and rock-hard, without an ounce of superfluous flesh. He showed off because she was watching him, diving in and then doing several lengths in a fast crawl, his arms cutting through the water and sending up a fine spray that glistened with the iridescence of cut crystal in the sun, each drop a prism of rainbow colours. As Cordelia sat and watched him, she wondered dispassionately whether or not to let him make love to her. That he would ask her some day soon she was quite sure; his kiss last night had told her that. All she had to decide was whether to say yes or no.

She wasn't in love with him, of course, that was for sure, and if she had sex with him that was all it would be—just sex, pure and simple. She might not even get any satisfaction out of it. Except the satisfaction of knowing that at least one man wanted her and found her attractive. And the intense, perverted sense of satisfaction at getting her own back on Marcus; because somehow letting Steve make love to her would be like aiming a blow at Marcus, even if she had to hurt herself to do it. I might even enjoy it, Cordelia mused as she watched Steve climb out of the other end of the pool and stand in the sunlight, legs apart, his hands on his hips. He waved to her and she lifted a lazy hand in return. He's obviously quite experienced and will probably be good in bed. He might even rid me of this frustration that's driving me crazy; make me able to live with myself again. Or even with him, she thought cynically. Maybe I'll like it so much I'll marry him and follow him from construction site to construction site all over the world.

Tears pricked at her eyes and she angrily wiped them away. Damn Marcus! I've done crying for him. But Steve wasn't Marcus and would never take his place. How could she possibly settle for anything less than love now that she had glimpsed it?

After lunch they dozed, then finished exploring the old city. On the way home they stopped at a seafood restaurant for dinner, Cordelia deliberately taking her time over the meal so that it was late before she got back. The next day Steve took her to the game reserve in the Yala National Park and the day after that to Galle on the south coast where they swam and sunbathed, wandered round the town and had a very English tea on the verandah of the New Oriental Hotel which, contrary to its name, was the oldest hotel in the whole of Sri Lanka.

Cordelia didn't even see Marcus during those three days, making sure that she left before he was around and going straight to her room when she got home in the evening, only slipping in to visit her father when she was quite sure he was alone. But as she was leaving the house the next day, Cordelia heard Marcus call her name. She hesitated for a fraction of a second and then kept on going, pretending that she hadn't heard him and hoping to get outside to where Steve was waiting before she had to face him. But the front door hadn't yet been opened for the day and she fumbled with the catches in her haste to get out.

'Cordelia.'

He was right behind her, there was no escape. Slowly she turned to face him. His appearance gave her a momentary shock of surprise: his eyes looked tired and there was a bleak, pinched look about his mouth. A great surge of emotion filled her heart, completely choked her so that she couldn't speak. She wanted to take him in her arms, kiss away the lines around his mouth, make him smile again. But then a small, cynical part of her mind told her that he was only tired through having sat up late, working on his book—or even working on Sugin, it added masochistically. Her face tightened as Cordelia answered coldly, 'Yes?'

'You're going out for the day again?' Marcus's eyes went over her, lingering on her defiant mouth.

'Yes. Steve's waiting for me outside.' She turned and reached up to fumble with the top catch of the door again.

'Here, let me.' Marcus reached past her and slid the catch back easily, but in doing so his hand covered hers.

Cordelia trembled convulsively and jerked her hand away as if his had been red-hot. She couldn't move away because she was trapped between Marcus and the angle of the doorway, but she swung round to face him defensively, her blue eyes large and vulnerable in her pale face.

He gazed down at her for a moment, then said abruptly, 'I have an invitation for you. Sugin is appearing in an exhibition of Sri Lankan dancing in Kandy tomorrow night. She's given me a ticket for you; she thinks you'll be interested to see what traditional Sri Lankan dancing is like.'

'Does she, indeed?' Cordelia remarked sarcastically, knowing full well that the other girl merely wanted to show off her gracefulness and beauty, and in so doing make Cordelia feel gauche in comparison. 'Sorry, I have a date with Steve tomorrow.'

'He's invited, too, of course.'

'I really don't think it's his scene. Now, if you'll excuse me . . .'

She turned to open the door, but Marcus put out a hand and held it shut. 'Don't you think you owe it to Sugin to go? You were damn rude about her dancing when we were all up at the Expatriates Club last week. The least you could do is to go and watch her and see for yourself whether what she said was justified.'

'I'm really not interested. I . . .'

'Coward!' Marcus put in derisively.

Cordelia glared at him. 'I'm no coward.'

'Aren't you? Then why are you afraid of going to watch her dance?'

No good telling him the truth, of course; that all Sugin wanted was to show herself off and that Cordelia didn't see why she should waste her time and pander to the other girl's vanity by doing what she wanted. He'd never believe her anyway, she thought resignedly. This time when she pulled at the door she took him by surprise and got it open, hurrying outside, her high-heeled sandals clattering on the smooth stone of the porch.

Steve was waiting at the wheel of his car and looked surprised when Marcus followed her outside.

'Sugin wants us to go to Kandy to watch her dance tomorrow night,' Cordelia told him abruptly. 'Do you want to go or not?'

His surprised look deepened as Steve got out of the car to join them. 'I don't mind.' He looked at Marcus. 'Are you going?'

'Yes. I'll be driving the girls there.'

'Okay, then I'll come along.'

Cordelia shot a malevolent glance at Marcus; the way he'd worded it had made it sound as if she had already accepted. '*We* don't have to go if you don't want to,' she said pointedly.

But Steve didn't pick up the signal. 'No, it suits me. There are plenty of places in Kandy where we can go afterwards, if you'd like to eat there.'

Disgusted with them both and wanting to get away from Marcus, Cordelia got into the car and sat waiting, but the two men stood talking for several minutes before Steve finally strolled round and got in beside her. They spent the day in Colombo, but for Cordelia it was already spoilt. She sat silently in her seat and when Steve tried to talk she snapped at him, so that he gave her a wary, concerned look and left her alone. After an hour or so she managed to pull herself together a little and by lunchtime was outwardly back to normal, but the thought of the coming outing to Kandy hung over her like a black cloud the whole day. They spent some time wandering around the big, colourful market in Colombo, then went to the Intercontinental Hotel again to swim and have lunch. It was Sunday and there was a whole crowd of Sri Lankans round the pool, obviously richer, better class people, from the clothes and jewels that they wore. They were mostly in family groups, but there were a few girls there, wearing Western one-piece bathing suits, all of them slim and graceful, with large dark eyes and smooth olive skin.

Cordelia watched them playing around in the water, laughing as they splashed each other. 'Steve, have you ever been out with any Sri Lankan girls?' she asked him.

He was lying on his stomach on the next lounger but raised himself on one elbow so that he could look at her. 'A couple of times. But the respectable girls are well chaperoned and the other kind just try and get as much money out of you as they can.'

'They're all very beautiful.'

Steve turned over and sat up so that he could see who she was looking at. 'Sure, when they're that age. They must be among the loveliest girls in the world. But then they get married pretty young, have to work hard and have a kid every year, so that they're old by the time they're thirty. Have you ever seen any of them who're still beautiful over the age of about twenty-five?'

'No, you're right, I haven't.' Cordelia smiled at him, her heart oddly comforted.

'And none of them—but none of them, can compare to a certain blonde English girl I know.' And he kissed her right there in front of everyone, then grinned and pulled her into the pool for another swim.

That night Steve asked her to sleep with him. Not that he just came out with it like that, he used a far more subtle approach.

'How about going to Adam's Peak to watch the dawn rise?'

'I don't know. It might be fun,' Cordelia replied without a great deal of enthusiasm. 'You don't mean now?'

'No. Some other time. It's too late now. You have to get to the rest-house halfway up the hill in the early evening, eat and spend part of the night there, and then climb to the top of the hill just before dawn. There are guides with torches to light the way for you.'

'Why can't you just drive up there and then climb the hill?'

'The road is too dangerous at night, there are lots of hairpin bends. You have to get there in daylight.' He had stopped the car at the side of the road while they watched hundreds of tiny fireflies, and now he put his arm round her and kissed her. 'We could really make it a night to remember,' he murmured, his mouth against her neck.

Cordelia sighed and moved away. 'I don't know. I'll think about it.'

He tried to persuade her, but Cordelia wouldn't commit herself either way, and eventually he restarted the car and drove on through the darkness, the coconut oil lamps in the houses they passed casting a mellowing glow in the warm night. Cordelia gazed out of the window unseeingly, wondering why life always turned out to be such a mess. If it had been Marcus who had made that suggestion to her she would have been ecstatically happy, but with Steve—somehow it could only be sordid.

First the bad news, then the good news: unfortunately Steve had to work the next day and Cordelia was dreading having to spend the day working in the same room as Marcus, but when she eventually summoned up enough courage to go out on to the verandah the next morning, she found him dressed in a suit and on the point of leaving.

'I have some business in Colombo to attend to,' he told her, setting down his coffee cup. 'But I'll be back in time to take you and Sugin to Kandy.'

'Are there any more chapters of the book ready that I can work on?' Cordelia asked, carefully avoiding looking directly at him.

To her surprise, he said, 'It's finished. I've started typing it from where you left off.' He paused, then added, 'I thought you might not want to spend any more time on it.'

Lifting her head, she looked at him steadily. 'I said I'd finish it for you and I meant it.'

Marcus seemed about to say something, then changed his mind and nodded. 'See you later, then.'

He must have worked very hard while she'd been out with Steve, Cordelia decided when she went into his study and saw the amount he'd got through. If she didn't know better she could have believed that he had devoted all his time to it, all day and far into the night. She got to work at once and found some comfort in the familiarity of it, the need to concentrate to the exclusion of all else.

By working solidly all day, she finished several chapters and left only a small pile to do—perhaps a morning's work.

They weren't having dinner at the bungalow that evening, there wouldn't be time before they left for Kandy, so at four Cordelia joined her father on the verandah for half an hour before going in to change. He seemed much better, able to walk around the garden a little, and spend as long as he liked outside, but his old restlessness seemed to have returned with his strength. Now he wanted to be completely fit again and was impatient with his own weakness.

At length Cordelia left him and went in to change. She put on a cream silk, sleeveless blouse and a matching straight linen skirt, with high-heeled sandals that looked good now that her legs were so beautifully brown. Even if I get nothing else out of this trip, at least I got a tan, she thought cynically as she checked her appearance in the full-length mirror in her room. She put on a minimum of make-up, just eye-shadows and lightener, mascara and a touch of lipstick, she really didn't need much when she was so brown, but her hair she washed and tonged into soft, loose waves around her head.

Marcus must have come home while she was changing, because Steve arrived about ten minutes before he put in an appearance. Steve was in his usual lightweight slacks and a casual shirt, but when Marcus joined them in the sitting-room where they were having a drink while they waited, he was wearing a collarless, short-sleeved white shirt and a native sarong covering his legs and tied in a knot at his waist. Cordelia choked over her drink and Steve burst out laughing.

'You're not actually going to wear that thing?' he exclaimed.

'Why not?' Marcus answered, quite unperturbed. 'The hotel where the dancing takes place isn't air-conditioned and with all those people there it's going to be damned hot, I can tell you. And these sarongs are very practical in this climate. Why do you think the natives in most hot countries of the world wear them?'

'But don't you feel uncomfortable in it?'

'No. As a matter of fact it's a lot more comfortable and cooler than trousers. You ought to try it,' he added with a grin.

'No, thanks,' Steve said firmly. 'I just hope for your sake it doesn't fall down. The native boys up at the dam site seem to spend half their time refolding the things and doing them up again when they come loose.'

Marcus laughed. 'I assure you I won't embarrass you.'

'Hey,' said Steve, going across to him. 'There's something I always wanted to know. Somebody told me that these sarongs are like kilts and they don't wear anything underneath. Now, is that true?'

'Wouldn't you like to know?' Marcus taunted him. 'The only way you're going to find out is if you get one for yourself. Then I'll tell you.'

The two men continued to rib one another for a few minutes and then Sugin made her entrance. She didn't simply walk in, but came to the French doors from the garden and stood in the doorway, the setting sun behind her, wearing a beautiful golden sari with a little matching blouse which left her midriff bare. Her face was heavily made up, ready for her performance, a great many bracelets jangled on her wrists and she wore large earrings with green stones.

There was the hush she'd wanted as she posed in the doorway, and then she stepped into the room as Marcus moved to welcome her. He complimented Sugin on her appearance and Steve followed suit, then the Sri Lankan girl turned to Cordelia with a scarcely-concealed sneer, as if she expected the other girl to stay silent, but Cordelia, too, said, 'You look very—exotic. Very Eastern,' which Sugin didn't quite know how to take.

Marcus gave a thin-lipped smile as he watched the two of them. Coming across to take her empty glass, he said to Cordelia, 'And you look very Western,' which she didn't know how to take, either. Then he grinned at Steve. 'It seems we have the best of both worlds tonight.'

During the drive to Kandy, Cordelia sat in the back with Steve, and as soon as they got to the hotel where the display was to be held, Sugin disappeared round the back to change into her first costume. Cordelia had expected something rather grander than the big third-floor room with rows of old, hard wooden chairs set out in front of a stage that didn't have any curtains, the lighting coming from a row of primitive-looking electric lamps strung along the front. Tacked on the wall at the back of the stage was a big Sri Lankan flag with its angry, symbolic lion, but apart from this the stage had no other furniture.

A slim, very neatly dressed youth showed them to the seats that had been reserved for them in the front row. There were already quite a few people there, nearly all tourists, being escorted to their seats by couriers from the various package holiday companies, many of them complaining because

they wouldn't be able to get a good view or didn't
have a clear field of vision for their cameras. The
performance was about a quarter of an hour late
in starting and by then the room was very hot,
even though all the windows were open. Cordelia
wished she had brought a fan like some of the
other women, but had to make do with the
programme she had been handed as she came in
and which listed the first item as 'Bolowing of the
Conchshell: tradtional welcome and drum orchstra
(By man).' And she could only hope that the music
would be better than the spelling.

The first men came on in traditional dress, the
notes of the drums differing because of the skins
with which they were made; there was little tune to
it and it was very repetitive, so that after a while it
jarred on your ears. Sugin made her first
appearance in a dance entitled 'Pooja Dance:
Dance paying homage to the Buddha Doities and
Guru (Dancing teecher) (By Girls).' There were
three dancers, and Sugin was the middle one. They
were all three equally graceful, beautiful and well
rehearsed; Cordelia could well understand that
they had to be taught the dances from an early
age, for each movement of the body, of hands and
of feet, was to a set pattern. It was interesting, it
was very watchable, but to Cordelia it was too
stylised, it lacked life and spontaneity, there was
no emotion in it; the girls seemed to know the
movements so well that they performed them
automatically, their minds on other things, their
eyes on the audience, gauging its reaction.

There were fourteen dances on the programme
and by halfway through nearly everyone in the
place was oozing with perspiration and longing for
a drink, but all there was to be had was warm

Coke which you bought beforehand and which
had to be drunk straight out of the bottle, without
even a straw. Cordelia looked at the rust marks on
the neck of her bottle and handed it to Steve, who
took it gratefully. Marcus gave him an 'I told you
so' grin; he was still cool in his loose clothing.

The programme was a long one, it lasted over two
hours without a break, the hard wooden chairs
growing harder by the minute. Cordelia shifted
uncomfortably, hot and sticky, the discordant
banging of the drums and the wail of the flutes
grating on her nerves and giving her a headache. She
longed for it to end, and even more for a long, cold
drink. When it did at last finish with what was
described as a 'Group Dance: perfomed by men and
girls', the three of them, of one accord, headed for
the bar on the ground floor of the hotel where there
were at least a couple of electric fans to cool the place
down. A youth in the doorway tried to take her
programme back, but Cordelia hung on to it: its bad
spelling and funny English had been the only
highlight in the whole evening so far.

Steve bought her a cocktail with an arrack base;
Cordelia downed it almost in one go. 'God, I
needed that!' she declared fervently. Marcus and
Steve both laughed at her vehemence. Looking up,
she caught Marcus's eye and her heart jumped
crazily, then began beating very fast. 'Do you
think I could have another one of those?' she
asked unsteadily. Sugin kept them waiting for
nearly half an hour and during that time Cordelia
had two more cocktails, the drinks acting on her
empty stomach and going straight to her head.
They ate in a nearby restaurant and had a fish
curry, which was so hot that they needed several
bottles of the local beer to cool it down.

'Here, sprinkle some shredded coconut on it,' Steve advised her. 'That's what the natives use to take the sting out of it.'

Cordelia looked round at the tables where parties of Sri Lankans were scooping their food up with their fingers, never having learnt to use knives and forks. She pushed her plate away. 'Thanks, but I can't manage any more; my mouth is on fire as it is!'

Sugin looked at her contemptuously. 'Your Western food is tasteless; you should use spices in your cooking.'

'If you've been brought up on curries like these, I'm not surprised that you find our food tasteless. I doubt whether you have any palate left at all. But then,' Cordelia added, 'we don't usually have to disguise the taste of rotten fish or meat.'

Steve had been about to eat a lump of fish, but now he paused, then lowered his fork and pushed his plate away. 'God, I don't think I want any more either.' Then he looked at Cordelia and they both burst out laughing.

They began to tell each other about all the worst foods they had ever tasted, vying with one another to find the most terrible. It was wicked to do so while the other two were still eating, but Cordelia didn't care; she felt in a reckless, frivolous mood and didn't much care what she said or did. They laughed uproariously over frogs' legs and sheep's eyeballs, and Steve knew of some really yeuky dishes which were so improbable that she accused him of making them up. By the time they left the restaurant she was giggling helplessly and in no mood to go tamely back to the bungalow.

'Let's go on somewhere,' she demanded. 'Surely there must be a night club or something here.'

'I do not wish to go to a night club,' Sugin said petulantly. 'I wish to go home. I am very tired after my performance.'

'We're all going back,' Marcus said grimly. 'Come on, the car's . . .'

'I said I'm not going.' Cordelia glared at him, rocking a little unsteadily but supported by Steve's arm.

'And just how do you expect to get back home late at night?' Marcus demanded, his eyes darkening with anger.

'We'll take a taxi—that's if we bother to come back tonight at all,' Cordelia replied shortly, her chin coming up in defiance.

Marcus took a furious step towards her. 'You don't know what you're saying. You've had too much to drink.'

'So what? What the hell has it got to do with you how much I drink?' she shouted, both of them now oblivious of the others.

'You'll do as you're damn well told!' Marcus reached out and grabbed her wrist, began to pull her towards the car.

'Hey, now wait a minute!' Steve put an arm round her waist and pulled the other way, so that she felt like a rope in a tug-of-war.

Marcus turned on Steve with a snarl that stopped him in his tracks. 'You keep out of this!' Then he glared at Cordelia. 'Are you coming, or do I have to pick you up and carry you?'

Ordinarily Cordelia would have thought before she spoke, would have hesitated before such anger, but now she was much too furious herself to care. 'No, I'm not!' she yelled at him. 'I'm going with Steve.' With a jerk she pulled her wrist free of his hand, then pointed derisively at his sarong.

'You've really gone native, haven't you? Well, why don't you just—just run along with your little native girl and leave me alone?'

Marcus's face twisted with rage and for a frightened second she shrank away from him as it looked as if he was going to do as he threatened, but then he swore savagely, turned on his heel and strode towards the car, Sugin hastily trotting after him with such a punch-drunk look on her face that it was almost funny.

Steve was equally astounded. 'What the hell was all that about?' he demanded as they watched the car pull away much too fast.

'I—I don't really know,' Cordelia muttered hollowly. She felt suddenly flat and exhausted, as if her blood had stopped flowing.

'I didn't know that you and Marcus were on the sort of terms where you could—well, that you disliked each other.'

'What? Oh, yes, we do. We—we can't stand one another,' Cordelia told him brokenly, her eyes still following the car out of sight.

Steve gave her a strange sort of look, as if he was seeing her for the first time all over again. 'We'd better go and find that night club.'

CHAPTER SEVEN

BUT they didn't find a night club. Instead they ended up at a hotel where several of the men Cordelia had met at the Expatriates Club were staying while on leave from the site. They were greeted uproariously and Cordelia found herself squashed on to a bench and a glass of beer put in her hand. The men had already had quite a lot to drink and were noisily and happily swapping experiences, telling jokes and singing. Some of the jokes would have made Cordelia's hair curl if they hadn't told her to cover her ears before the particularly rude ones. She sank with relief into the atmosphere, losing herself in it and glad to be just one of the boys for a while.

They broke up about three in the morning and Steve borrowed one of the men's cars to take her home. She was so tired that she staggered when she tried to walk and he had to help her out to it, and as soon as he got in beside her, her head slumped on to his shoulder and she fell asleep.

'Wake up, Cordelia, you're home.'

She sat up slowly and rubbed her stiff neck. Bright moonlight shone into the car. 'We're there already?'

'Yes. You all right?'

'Mm.' She yawned, but the sleep had done her good. 'Thanks for bringing me home. Shall I see you tomorrow?'

Steve gripped the steering wheel and said harshly, 'Is there any point?'

His tone made her look at him quickly. Her row with Marcus must have been very revealing, and Steve was no fool. Biting her lip, Cordelia looked away. 'No. I'm sorry.'

There was a minute's heavy silence before he said, 'Well, some you win, some you lose. But I would like to have won with you.' Leaning closer, he kissed her on the mouth. 'You'd better go in; I still have to drive back to the site.'

'I'm sorry, Steve,' she said again, but he merely gave a crooked kind of grin and reached past her to open the door.

Cordelia watched him go and then tried the front door. She wouldn't have been surprised to be locked out, but the door opened easily and quietly when she turned the handle.

Marcus was waiting for her in the sitting-room. He was sitting in an armchair, smoking a cigarette by the light of a single lamp, the ashtray beside him containing a small pile of cigarette ends. There was no newspaper or book in his hands to while away the time; he'd just been sitting there—waiting.

When Cordelia saw him she was immediately on the defensive. 'You don't have to say anything,' she said as he got to his feet. 'I'll leave here in the morning.'

'And go where?' Marcus bit out. 'Up to the site to live with Steve?'

'Where I'm going and who with is none of your damn business!'

A savage light came into his eyes as his temper exploded. He lunged forward, grabbing her arms and yanking her roughly towards him. 'Well, I'm about to make it my damn business!' And then he kissed her in a blaze of anger, hurting her deliberately, making her feel his strength.

'Let me go! You pig, let me go!' Cordelia twisted her head aside and tried to claw at him with her nails, but he pulled her arms behind her back and held her wrists imprisoned with one hand, using the other to grab a handful of her hair. Shaking with rage, he bent her against his braced body and forced her head back. Cordelia's mouth was open with the pain of his hold and her eyes blazed at him furiously. She hated him then, as she'd never in her life hated any man, and she began to struggle wildly, closing her mouth against him when he again tried to kiss her, her head jerking in a futile attempt to get free. His grip on her hair tightened so that she gasped in pain against his mouth, but still she kicked and writhed, even though she knew it was hopeless.

At last she quietened and he lifted his head to look at her. He was still terribly angry, she could feel it running through his body, see it in the grimness of his face. But now he knew that he had won and there was triumph too in his eyes. His fingers moved in her hair, turning her head into position for his last assault on her unprotected mouth. Slowly his head came down. He didn't close his eyes, but kept them on her until his hard mouth took hers and he opened her lips. Her surrender was complete; she hung limply in his arms, her strength drained away. Time seemed to stand still: he could have been kissing her for a minute or for an hour. Sound and sight had deserted her, she hung in a long black tunnel in which only the pressure of his body against hers was real. And it lit a fire deep within her that grew into an all-consuming flame. Her lips again moved against his, but this time in passion and need. He let go her arms and she slid them round his neck, clinging to him fiercely, wanting to lose herself for ever in his arms.

After a while, he bent and picked her up, carried her into her bedroom and shouldered the door shut behind them. They clung together for a long moment without speaking and then he gently took her arms from round his neck and began to undress her. He unbuttoned her blouse and slipped it off, and Cordelia shuddered as his hands touched her breasts, her hair tumbling round her neck. But her movement aroused him uncontrollably and his hands became urgent, as he took off the rest of her clothes, then his own, and lifted her on to the bed. He made love to her with a fierce passion that only became gentle and tender when his first hunger had been appeased. To Cordelia the night was a feast of rapture and she responded totally, as if the act of love with him was something she had waited for all her life. She yearned for him, ached for him, and only the mingling of their bodies in violent ecstasy could fulfil that need.

Afterwards, when he left her as the sun reached the pillows, Cordelia lay for a few moments in satiated happiness; she remembered the wide breadth of his shoulders, his weight as he pinned her to the bed, the salt taste of perspiration on his skin when she ran her tongue lightly across his chest. She recalled with joy how skilfully his hands had brought her to moaning arousal the second time, and how much—oh, God, how much! pleasure his mouth could give. She tried desperately to stay awake, to go on reliving the night, but exhaustion drew her into the flowing stream of sleep.

It was late when she woke, the sun high in the sky. For a moment she thought that it was just a dream, but then she saw the bruise marks on her skin, felt the stiffness in her body. Quickly she got out of bed, wanting to lie and dream about the hours they had spent in making love, but wanting even more to see Marcus again, to touch him, to know that he was close. She paused while towelling herself dry to look at her naked body in the long mirror. There were bruises, too, at the tops of her legs and red marks on her breasts where he had been rough with her in his first hunger. Cordelia covered the marks with a pair of shorts and a bikini top, then hurried out to find her lover.

As she stepped out on to the verandah the sun caught her and she paused, lifting up her face to bask in it, stretching her body like a long, golden animal.

'If you go on doing that I shall want to do what I did last night all over again.'

Opening her eyes, Cordelia saw Marcus sitting in one of the padded garden chairs. A sudden shyness overcame her, but he held out his hand and she ran to him. Pulling her down on to his lap, he kissed her possessively. 'You all right?' he asked, when he at last released her mouth.

She nodded, her head on his shoulder, her blue eyes gazing lovingly into his. 'It must be very late.'

'Mm. Much too late for breakfast; you'll have to wait till lunch.'

'Oh, lor', I'm starving. Maybe I'll eat you instead,' she told him, beginning to nibble his ear.

Marcus laughed. 'You took several bites out of me last night. Wildcat!' he added, giving her a playful punch on the jaw.

Cordelia caught his hand and gently opened his fist, entwining her fingers with his, marvelling at its strength and size compared to her own. She felt that she wanted to look at him all over in the daylight, to memorise each hair, each pore of his skin, to know his body as well as her own.

'What are you thinking?' Marcus demanded.

'That I want to know every little bit of you,' she admitted, kissing his fingers.

'Do you indeed? And which part would you like to start with?' he asked suggestively.

But she refused to be drawn. 'Oh, your hand will do.' She paused, then added rather breathlessly, 'For now.'

His fingers tightened on hers and his eyes darkened. Pulling her to him, he kissed her again.

Neither of them was aware of the houseboy's presence behind them until he coughed tactfully. 'The post has arrived, sir.'

'All right. Leave it on the table.'

The servant withdrew as quietly as he had come and Cordelia sat up. 'He saw us.'

'Do you mind?'

She looked at him in some surprise. 'No—but I thought you would.'

'Why?'

She almost said because of Sugin, but she wasn't going to spoil the day by doing that. 'Why else did you leave me and go back to your room this morning?' she countered.

'Only so that you could get some sleep. Single beds may be okay for making love, but they're not very comfortable for two people to sleep in.'

'I wouldn't have minded.' She lay back against his shoulder again. 'I'd like to wake up with you beside me.'

He smiled and kissed the tip of her nose. 'Your father was out here earlier. He seems to have something on his mind.'

'He's had something on his mind ever since he came to Sri Lanka,' Cordelia agreed with a sigh.

'Won't he tell you what it is?'

'No. He's never confided in me. We're not very close—but then you know that.'

'Yes.'

They talked a little longer about her father and then Cordelia got off his lap while he looked at his mail and the servant prepared the table for lunch. After the meal they took the car and Marcus drove inland, away from the roads used by the tourist traffic. They stopped to buy a king-coconut for a couple of rupees from a pedlar and Marcus cut a hole with his penknife in the top of the big, bright orange fruit, and they shared the juice, the liquid trickling down their chins. Where the road petered out, Marcus parked the car and they walked along the bed of a green, sun-filled valley where wild flowers grew in profusion and streams from the high hills above hurried along their rock beds. They came to a place where a high ledge jutted out and formed a waterfall with a small pool below it. Here Marcus kissed her and slowly took off her clothes. His mouth found her breast and she held his head there and groaned with delight, never wanting him to stop, but he took off his own things and led her under the waterfall.

The water was stingingly cold after the hot sun and made her gasp, but Marcus held her against him until her skin was used to the change and she had stopped shivering. Then he began to gently wash her all over, exploring the while with his hands, his eyes, his lips, until Cordelia discovered that it was quite possible for fire and water to exist together. Then he took her, there under the waterfall, her cries of pleasure lost beneath the noise of the cascading waters.

It was the beginning of days of unallayed happiness. Cordelia found Marcus to be a wonderful lover, very experienced but willing to teach her, guiding her hands so that she would know what to do to give him pleasure, and appreciative when she learnt quickly or used her own imagination. They talked a little, they ate a little, but they were greedy for each other's bodies and spent most of the time making love. It was as if each time, instead of satisfying their appetites, only made them hungry for more, as if they could never have enough of one another. And each time was different; different in emotion and intensity. Sometimes Marcus made love to her slowly, taking his time, gently caressing each part of her until she couldn't stand it any longer and cried out for him to take her. Then he would tease her a little, pretending that he'd changed his mind, until she grew desperate and pushed him down on to the bed and *made* him love her. Sometimes he was like the first time, so eager and hungry for her that he took her with a demanding ferocity, his strength hurting her a little, and perhaps Cordelia liked it that way the best of all, because it was then, as his body jerked in uncontrollable climax, that he groaned out, 'Oh God, Cordelia. I love you! I love you!' He murmured endearments to her often, paid her compliments that frequently brought a flush to her cheeks, but they were the only times he said that he loved her.

They spent one morning working on the book until it was finished and then ceremoniously parcelled it up and took it to the post office to send to England. And, of necessity, they both spent some time with her father, but he seemed preoccupied and quite willing for them to leave him alone in the house. Marcus told her he had asked if he might use the phone, but they never saw him do so, so guessed that he must wait until they were out of the way.

'Did he say who he wanted to call?' Cordelia asked.

'No, but he asked for directories for the whole island.'

'How strange. I wonder what he's doing?' But Cordelia only puzzled over it for a few moments. When Marcus took her hand and led her into the garden she forgot about it completely. Just as she had forgotten about Sugin; the other girl hadn't been to the house since their first night together and she supposed that Marcus had ordered her to stay away. But after that first day she hadn't even thought about her, she was too high, too much living on a cloud to let unpleasant thoughts mar her happiness.

One day they got up very early and drove across to the eastern side of the island to the long, almost deserted golden beaches near Trincomalee, where the only shade was from the palm trees which grew on the edge of the shoreline. Marcus drove on past the beaches near the few tourist hotels until they found a small, secluded cove to themselves. There he insisted they take off their clothes, and Cordelia experienced for the first time the wonderfully free sensation of swimming naked, felt the warm blue water caress her body almost as sensuously as Marcus had. She also experienced for the first time what it was like to be laid down in the shallows and be made love to as the little waves rippled over them.

They lay close together on a huge beach towel, soaking up the sun, and Cordelia said dreamily, 'Will it always be like this?'

Marcus smiled and raised himself on one elbow, his eyes running over her nakedness in quiet pride of possession. 'Do you want it to be?'

'Yes. Oh, yes!' She spoke in a fervent, heartfelt tone, unable now to imagine any life but this.

'Then it will be,' he answered simply.

Cordelia thought about it for a moment and then sat up and looked at him. 'How, Marcus? What will we do when my father's well enough to leave here?'

'Don't let's worry about that now.' He lay back and reached up to caress her breasts. 'Why think about the future when the present is so perfect?' He began to pull her down on top of him. 'Come here, my beautiful, golden girl.' She smiled and without the slightest hesitation, did what he wanted.

The next night they dined at the bungalow and afterwards went for a walk in the garden. When they came to the frangipani tree Marcus again leant against its trunk, as he had that night when he had first kissed her with such passion, a night that seemed a lifetime ago. But now he brought it back by saying softly as he took her in his arms, 'Do you remember when we kissed under this tree—when we'd been to Sigiriya to see the Cloud Maidens?'

'Of course. I wanted you so badly. I thought you were going to take me to bed with you that night. Why didn't you? Didn't you want me then?'

'Are you crazy? God, you were driving me so wild that I near as dammit tore off your clothes and made love to you here on the ground!' For a moment his hands tightened on her arms, then relaxed. 'But it seemed wrong for all sorts of reasons. You were so young, and I didn't want to take advantage of you. And when you give, you give all of yourself—holding nothing back. Even that first time you spoke of love. But I wasn't ready for that sort of commitment.'

'So you decided to introduce me to Steve?'

'Mm.' He ran a hand absently through her hair. 'But then every time I saw you with him or thought about you together I got more and more jealous until it all blew up in my face and I couldn't stand it any longer.'

Cordelia laughed happily and put her arms round his neck. 'So you took me for yourself. It would have been a lot better if you'd done what we both wanted that first time. But you can always make up for it now,' she added, moving her thighs voluptuously against his.

His hands came down on to her hips. 'Are you suggesting what I think you are, Miss Allingham?' he demanded, his voice thickening.

'Oh, yes, Mr Stone,' Cordelia agreed breathlessly, feeling his body already start to harden. 'I am. Most definitely.'

'Well, in that case . . .' He laid her down on the grass among the fallen frangipani petals. 'No gentleman would ever disoblige a lady.'

It was much later when they crept back through the house to her bedroom, and the next morning, when he went to leave her, Cordelia clung to him and wouldn't let him go. 'Please stay with me,' she begged.

'I have an appointment with the bank in Colombo,' he reminded her.

'But you don't have to leave yet,' she coaxed. 'Just one more time.'

'He laughed. 'Woman, you're insatiable!' But he lay back beside her.

'Oh, Marcus, I love you. Is it wrong to want each other so much?'

'Wrong? Of course not. My darling girl, you're one in a million. The kind a man dreams of all his life but only a few are lucky enough to find: beautiful, sexy and intelligent.'

'Am I really sexy?'

He looked at her in mock seriousness. 'Perhaps, madam, you would like me to demonstrate yet again just how sexy I find you?'

'Oh, yes,' Cordelia agreed fervently. 'Yes, please!'

When they finally woke, cramped together in the narrow bed, the sun was already high in the sky. Marcus groaned and looked at his watch. 'My God, look at the time! Where the hell are my clothes?' He found his trousers and pulled them on, then turned to kiss her. ' 'Bye, darling, see you later. Lord, I wish I didn't have to go,' he added softly as he gazed down at her languorous eyes, her golden hair forming an aureole around her head.

'Don't, then. Stay with me,' she murmured.

'Jezebel! But I'll soon be back.' He kissed her again and Cordelia lifted his hand to her breast. He caressed her with growing passion, then with an oath tore himself away and went into the bathroom to shower. She smiled and lay there contentedly, drifting off to sleep again after she heard his car drive away.

She slept for another hour or so and woke feeling on top of the world, jumping out of bed and already counting the hours until Marcus would return. What would they do today? she wondered. Maybe they'd go to the famous botanical gardens in Kandy, a trip Marcus had promised her for some time. But there were bound to be lots of people there and they wouldn't be able to make love for hours and hours, so maybe they wouldn't go there after all. Cordelia laughed happily and whistled a tune as she showered and washed her hair. Putting on a bathrobe, she went back to her bedroom—and stopped dead in her tracks. Sugin was in the room, standing by the bed.

After a stunned moment, Cordelia burst out, 'What are you doing here? Get out of my room at once!'

But the other girl didn't answer, just stared at her stonily, and then Cordelia saw that she was holding Marcus's shirt. It had a grass stain on it where they had made love in the garden last night; that, and the tumbled bed, told their own story.

After a long moment in which Cordelia just looked at her helplessly, Sugin broke the silence by saying bitterly, 'So he is your lover. That's why he told me not to come here any more.'

'I'm sorry,' Cordelia answered inadequately. 'But, you see, we love each other and . . .'

Sugin's harsh laughter cut off her words. 'Love? You really think he loves you, you stupid English girl? He takes you only because you're easy, cheap. Because you will give yourself to any man who wants you.'

'How dare you?' Cordelia demanded furiously. 'Get out of here. Do you hear me? Get out of this house!'

But Sugin faced her obstinately. 'You cannot

order me to do what you want, English girl. You are not the mistress here and never will be.'

'Not yet, maybe,' Cordelia retorted angrily. 'But when Marcus and I are married, I'll . . .'

'Married?' Sugin laughed spitefully. 'Do you really think that he intends to marry you?'

'Yes. Yes, I do,' Cordelia replied without hesitation, but rather taken aback by Sugin's vehement tone.

Jeeringly the other girl went on, 'He will never marry you, English girl. How can he—when he already has a wife?'

The room seemed to go suddenly cold and fade away around her so that Cordelia could see nothing but Sugin's spiteful, jeering face. 'I don't—I don't believe you,' she said dully.

'No? Then I'll prove it to you. Come.' She led the way into Marcus' bedroom, a room in which Cordelia herself had only been in to once or twice, and then only for a few moments while Marcus was there. Sugin went straight over to a small desk and opened the right-hand lower drawer, took out a bundle of letters and shoved them at Cordelia. 'See, the address on the back. From Mrs Annette Stone.'

'They could be from his mother,' Cordelia said faintly. 'Or—or a sister-in-law.'

'He has no mother. Or any brothers,' Sugin told her viciously. 'Don't you even know that about him yet? You still don't believe me? Come, I'll show you.' She took Cordelia's unresisting wrist in a rough grip that hurt and pulled her into the study. 'Look.' She went to an old unmarked box file that was lying on a bottom shelf and that Cordelia hadn't ever noticed before. Inside were some old notepads and a scrapbook of press cuttings and book reviews. Sugin quickly turned the pages of press cuttings and stopped at a photograph. 'There!' she said triumphantly.

The photo was dated seven years ago and showed a younger Marcus without the sardonic lines around his mouth. He was smiling happily down at the girl who stood beside him; a slim, dark-haired girl who was laughing excitedly, her eyes on the camera. The caption under the picture said, 'Marcus Stone, whose latest book *The Gateway to Hell* has just sold a million copies, with his wife Annette at the Foyles' Literary Lunch given in his honour'.

The world seemed to explode into a grey mist through which she had to grope her way, but somehow Cordelia found herself back in her own room, alone, and with the door locked behind her. She sat there, huddled into a chair for a long time, then numbly got up, dressed and packed her clothes.

James Allingham was sitting at a table in his room when she knocked and went in to see him. He had several papers spread out before him, together with a map of the island. He looked up with a frown, then saw her white face and said, 'Is anything the matter?'

'Yes. I'm leaving here,' Cordelia answered baldly.

'Why?'

'That doesn't matter. I'm going back to England.'

'I'd rather you didn't. Cordelia, there's something I want to tell you. It's about why I wanted to come out here.'

Cordelia stared at him. 'You want to tell me that now?' she demanded angrily. 'Now? After all this time? Well, I'm not interested. I'm going back to England.'

'Please.' He looked at her in some distress. 'Has something happened between you and Marcus? I couldn't help noticing that you were—well, very friendly.'

Cordelia nodded, unable to put it into words. 'And now I just want to get away from here.'

'All right, but will you please stay in Sri Lanka? Just for a short time. I shall be well enough to leave here soon. There's something I have to do, something I've already put in hand, and then we'll be able to travel back together, although it will probably have to be by sea.'

'All right,' Cordelia agreed, quite indifferent to where she went. 'I'll phone you when I find somewhere.'

He gave her some money and she left him, cutting him short when he again tried to tell her his reasons for coming to Sri Lanka. The taxi she had ordered arrived soon after and she left without any fuss, not even looking back to see if Sugin was triumphantly watching her departure. She told the driver to take her to Negombo on the west coast, a highly popular tourist area where she could lose herself among all the other Europeans. The road was the same one that led to Colombo, and after they had been driving along it for an hour or so she recognised Marcus's car going in the other direction, back to the bungalow. He was driving fast and there was an eager, expectant look on his face.

Cordelia leant back in her seat and he didn't see her, was too impatient to get home to look into passing cars. But what a surprise he would get when he arrived and found her gone. He would just have to make do with his native girl again until some other gullible fool came along, Cordelia thought with bitter cynicism.

CHAPTER EIGHT

CORDELIA booked into one of the tourist hotels just outside Negombo without any difficulty and went straight to her room. It was much hotter here on the coast than in the hill country, but the room was air-conditioned and felt reasonably cool. She didn't bother to unpack or anything, but just lay down on the bed and gazed up at the white-painted ceiling. She must, she supposed, have been incredibly stupid, but it had honestly never occurred to her to wonder if Marcus was married. He had never spoken of a wife, of a family. Had he any children? No, if he had Sugin would have been bound to taunt her with that too.

Oh, God, she'd been such a fool! But she loved him so much. The thing that hurt most, of course, was that he hadn't been honest with her, hadn't told her himself that he wasn't free. She had given herself to him so eagerly, so trustingly, certain that what they had was so strong that nothing could break it, that they would be together for ever, and now she felt that her trust had been betrayed. She had taken it for granted that she and Marcus would marry, when her father was better, when they all went back to England. There hadn't been any feeling of urgency; the world was standing still for them and the 'now' was so perfect that the future was too far away to even think about. He hadn't said that they would marry in so many words, of course, but there hadn't been any need to, it had been explicit in his eyes, his touch, his lovemaking. And he *had* said that it would go on for ever; wasn't that the same as saying that they would spend the rest of their lives together? But he hadn't meant it, must have been lying through his teeth just to keep her sweet. Miserably Cordelia turned her head into the pillow and wept.

She stayed in her room all that day and most of the next, either out on the balcony or on the bed, but by the evening of the second day she began to feel giddy and realised that she would have to go down and eat. Red-clothed tables were set out on the open terrace only ten yards or so from the beach and there was a cool breeze from the sea. A trio of Latin-American singers moved among the tables, playing the guests' requests on their guitars. Cordelia was given a table to herself and ordered some food, forcing herself to eat it. The waiters, all slim and young, seeing that she was alone, tried to persuade her to go to the night club in the hotel that evening, but she just shook her head silently and they left her alone.

After the meal she went back to her room and picked up the phone, hesitated a moment, then dialled the number for the bungalow. Marcus's voice answered and wrenched her heart so cruelly that for several moments she couldn't speak. He repeated the number and she managed to say, 'James Allingham, please.'

'Cordelia! Cordelia, is that you?' Marcus demanded sharply.

'I want to speak to my father.'

'Cordelia, where are you? You *must* tell me!'

With a sob, she slammed the receiver back on its rest, unable to take any more.

She tried to phone again, an hour or so later, and this time the houseboy answered. 'Mr Allingham, please.'

After a short wait her father came on the line.
'Hallo.'

'It's Cordelia. I've booked into a hotel near
Negombo.'

'What's it called?'

'Brown's Beach. But don't tell Marcus.'

'Very well, if that's what you want. Are you all
right?'

'Yes. How are you?'

'Oh, progressing.' But he sounded tired. 'Look,'
he added rather awkwardly, 'Marcus is here. He'd
like to speak to you. He wants to know why you
left. It seems you didn't leave him a note or give
any explanation before you went.'

'No. I don't want to speak to him.'

'But I really feel that you owe him that much.'

'No! I don't owe him anything!' Cordelia
retorted vehemently.

'But he's been very kind to us. I don't have to
remind you of that. Won't you at least speak to
him—tell him why you left?'

'No. I won't speak to him. But you can—but
you can ask him how his wife is.' And then she put
down the phone, her hands trembling so much
that she almost dropped it.

Cordelia spent all the long, hot days close to the
hotel, only leaving it to take solitary walks along
the endless golden beach, her bare feet sinking into
the wet sand and making footprints that were
immediately wiped away by the next wave. Most
days she went out to the pool to swim and
sunbathe on a lounger, her skin becoming darker
as her hair bleached to a lighter shade of gold.
Sometimes a man would try to pick her up, but he
had only to look at the desolation in her eyes to
know that it was hopeless and turn and go away.

At the weekend she saw two faces that she knew: men from the Expatriates Club who were friends of Steve's. Cordelia managed to avoid them, but she wasn't sure whether or not they'd seen her. Not that it mattered—nothing mattered now.

Every day she expected the promised phone call from her father, and as the days passed and lengthened into a week she began to wonder if he was having difficulty in finishing the business he had said he had still to do here. She wished now that she had listened when he was going to tell her what it was. Often her eyes went to the phone as she wondered whether she ought to call him again. But she was afraid that Marcus might answer and so she left it, telling herself that he must ring soon.

Then, one evening, at about nine o'clock, there was a knock on her door. Cordelia had already been down to dinner and was sitting on the balcony, her eyes closed, listening to the sound of the waves pounding on the shore and above it the music from a band of musicians who were playing for all the people who were still eating down on the terrace. She was wearing a turquoise-blue halter-neck dress with a full soft skirt, not because she had chosen to wear it but because it was the first thing that came to hand. The knock came again and she reluctantly got up to answer it, thinking that it was the maid who came round every evening to spray the room with insecticide to kill any mosquitoes that might have got in during the day. Pulling back the bolt, she opened the door and began to say, 'Okay, you can . . .' then stopped dead, frozen with shock.

Marcus stood in the doorway, a hard, set look on his face. Before she had recovered enough to move, he strode into the room so that she had to move backwards to get out of the way. Then he shut the door firmly behind him.

'What—what do you want? We have nothing to say to each other.' Cordelia's hands were trembling and she had to ball them into tight fists in the hope that he wouldn't see.

'On the contrary, I have a great deal to say to you,' Marcus told her grimly. 'But it will have to wait. Right now, I'm afraid I have some bad news for you.'

'Bad news?' Cordelia saw in his face a mixture of seriousness and compassion and knew at once that her father had died. 'Oh!' For a moment she couldn't take it in, then she said on a note of protest, 'But he was getting better! He said he'd soon be well enough to go home.'

'He was. But yesterday he wanted me to take him—he wanted to do something before he left, something that involved quite a long car ride. I didn't want him to, but he insisted. He was all right, or he seemed to be, but later on, in the evening, he had another heart attack and he died early this morning.'

Cordelia slowly sat down on the bed. 'Did he—do what he wanted?'

'Yes.'

'I'm glad.'

She sat silently for several minutes while Marcus stood watching her, then he said, 'The funeral has been arranged for tomorrow.'

'So soon?' But then she remembered that in this hot climate funerals had to take place quickly. 'Yes, of course.' She tried to gather her wits. 'Where?'

'In Nuwara Eliya. There's a Protestant burial ground there.' He looked at her for a moment and then round the room. 'Shall I help you to pack?'

Cordelia stared at him stupidly. It still hadn't sunk in that her reason for staying here was gone, that she no longer had anyone to wait for. 'But you said the funeral wasn't till tomorrow.'

'No, but I'll take you back with me now. There won't be time for you to travel out there tomorrow.' Crossing to the wardrobe, he took out one of her suitcases and put it on the other bed, began to pack some of her things into it.

'Wait—I can do that myself.' But he insisted on helping her, and almost before she knew it, Cordelia found herself at the desk, paying her bill and checking out.

As they drove along she realised that Marcus had hurried her deliberately, giving her no time to think, but now she had to face the fact that she was going to be alone with him at the bungalow again, unless . . . She turned to him, 'Is Sugin still—with you?'

'If you mean is she at the bungalow, then no. She's gone to live with her sister—for good.'

'You mean she isn't coming back?'

'No. And she never was with me—in the way that you mean,' he added tersely.

They were both silent then for several miles until Cordelia said with difficulty, 'My father was going to tell me his reasons for coming here, but at the time I—I wasn't very interested. Did he tell you, then, what they were?'

'Yes, he did.' Cordelia waited expectantly, but after a pause Marcus went on, 'I think perhaps it would be better if I left the explanations until tomorrow. It's a bit complicated.'

'All right.'

They lapsed into silence again, but it was a restless silence which lay between them like a tangible thing. They had been so close but were now so far apart, neither of them willing to speak about what had happened and release the flood of words and emotions it would bring. Now was not the time nor the place—for Cordelia there would never be one, so they both stayed silent during the long drive through the night.

When they got to the bungalow, the houseboy opened the door as soon as the car drew up and gave her such a warm and sympathetic greeting that for the first time she felt close to tears. He took her cases out of the car and carried them into her old room. Cordelia opened her mouth to protest, but then realised that there was no alternative. Marcus was looking at her questioningly, so she quickly turned and went into the sitting-room. He followed her and closed the door. 'Would you like a drink?'

She shook her head and went to sit in a chair that had its back to the garden, her hands gripped together tightly in her lap. 'Is my father—is he still here?' she asked with difficulty.

'No. His body has been taken to Nuwara Eliya. Do you want to see him before the funeral?'

'No. Oh, no,' she said hastily, recalling how she had been taken to see her mother after she died and could never then remember her alive.

'Very well.' Marcus poured himself a drink and sat opposite her, his face dark and shadowed, making the lines around his mouth appear deeper than they had been. 'Is there anything else you want to know?'

'Did he—tell you where I was staying?'

'Yes, towards the end. I'd begged him to tell me before, but he wouldn't—not until after he had the heart attack and knew he would never be going back to England. Then he told me.'

The bitterness in his tone made her quickly glance at him, but his eyes were fixed on her so she looked away again, her heart beginning to beat faster. If he had begged her father to tell him where she was he must have wanted to see her quite badly. She swallowed and changed the subject. 'You said he told you why he came here?'

'Yes.' Marcus looked down at the glass in his hand, swirled the liquid in it, as if he was trying to make up his mind, then he said, 'Did your mother ever tell you why she left your father?'

Cordelia lifted her head in surprise. 'She didn't actually leave him—she just couldn't take the climate here.'

'That may have been what you were told at the time, but—according to your father—it wasn't the real reason.'

'What do you mean? What was the reason, then?'

'It seems that your father had an affair with a local girl, the daughter of one of the workers on the tea plantation. It lasted for some time and was quite serious—so serious that he asked your mother for a divorce, but she wouldn't give it to him. Instead she tried to break up his affair, but when that didn't work she sent you to England and later cleared out herself. Your father admitted that the whole thing was his fault, entirely his fault, but he was infatuated with this girl. And,' Marcus went on slowly, his eyes fixed on her stunned face, 'there were two children of their— liaison.'

'Two children?' Cordelia stood up agitatedly. 'I can't believe it! Why didn't my mother tell me?'

'Possibly because she didn't know. I gather that
the children were born after she left, but then the
mother died and it was thought best for them to be
brought up by her brother, who adopted them as
his own.'

'But they're still here—in Sri Lanka?'

'Yes. Of course your father had to leave when
the tea plantations were nationalised. He sent
them money from time to time, but then the
family moved and he lost touch with them.
That's why he wanted to come back here—to
find them and to make sure that their future was
secure.'

'I see.' Cordelia sat down on the edge of a chair.
'And he found them all right?'

'Yes. He contacted people he used to know here
and with their help managed to find them. Then he
arranged with a solicitor to settle some money on
them. That was where I took him yesterday—and
to see the children.'

'Do they know he's their father?'

'No.' Marcus shook his head. 'And it was his
wish that they never would.'

'But I don't understand why he brought me here
with him.'

Marcus got up and poured himself another
drink, then glanced at Cordelia a moment and
filled another glass. He handed it to her and she
took it automatically, looking at him enquiringly.
'The settlement was part of his will. As his next-of-
kin you were bound to find out about it. Also it
meant that he would have less to leave you. He
wanted to explain to you about that, and I think
he felt he could do that best if you were here and
could see for yourself how poor the people are.'

'Was he afraid that I'd contest it or something?'

Shrugging, Marcus said, 'I don't know. I think he just wanted everything to be in order before he died.'

'But coming here and putting things in order killed him,' Cordelia pointed out. 'Why couldn't he have told me from the start?'

'Maybe he was afraid that you'd react like your mother and have nothing to do with him.'

'Was he? I'm surprised he even bothered with me when it was his other family that he loved,' she said bitterly.

'But he loved you,' Marcus told her earnestly. 'Otherwise he would never have stayed with your mother so long. He told me that the marriage had been unhappy from the start. And, believe me, there's no point in trying to hold together a marriage that's fallen apart,' Marcus said heavily, his voice sounding strange.

'He could have come to see me,' Cordelia said unhappily. 'He could have written.'

'He told me that he wanted to, but your mother wouldn't let him. And then after she died your aunt just took you over, and you were so cold and distant towards him that he thought he'd lost you.' He paused, but when she didn't speak, added, 'Perhaps he hoped that you would get to know each other again while you were here.'

Cordelia laughed harshly. 'That's ridiculous! You saw how he was. He never once made any— any offers of reconciliation, if you like. Quite the opposite. He was almost always brusque and short with me.'

'Maybe he didn't know how. He was a proud man, Cordelia. Maybe he could have used some help from you.'

Cordelia stiffened and put down her glass. 'You seem to have got to know him extremely well,' she remarked sarcastically.

'Yes, I did—after you ran away. We spent a lot of time together—when I wasn't scouring every hotel in every town I could think of, trying to find you,' Marcus said grimly.

Cordelia's face paled. She stood up, a little unsteadily. Marcus put a hand under her elbow, but she jerked her arm away. 'Don't touch me!' she flared angrily.

His face darkened and for a moment she thought he was going to force the issue, but then he stepped back. 'You're tired,' he said curtly. 'You'd better go to bed. We'll talk tomorrow.'

She glared at him for a moment, then suddenly all defiance left her, so she just nodded and went to her room. But just walking into it brought back so many memories; memories of the most ecstatic lovemaking, of words said, of caresses exchanged. In a semi-automatic state, she washed and changed into pyjamas, but it took a sheer effort of will to get into bed and turn off the light. And then she lay there, in the bed they had shared so often, knowing that Marcus was only a few feet away, her body crying out for him, and the memories came and engulfed her so that she lay awake far, far into the night.

To Cordelia's surprise there were quite a lot of people at the funeral. Many of them introduced themselves as friends of her father from his tea plantation days, and she guessed that these were the people he had contacted to help him find his other family. All of them said they remembered her as a child, so that she was touched and grateful to them. They all came back to the bungalow to lunch afterwards, and as several of them knew who Marcus was, he was kept busy answering questions about his work.

It was gone three before the last one left. Cordelia politely shook hands with them and watched their car until it turned out of the gate, then gave a sigh of relief and immediately turned and hurried inside the house.

'Cordelia!'

Marcus called after her, but she took no notice, going straight to her room and locking the door. Quickly she changed out of the black and white dress which was the only suitable thing she had had to wear, and put on a short-sleeved shirt and a pair of jeans. The rest of her things she packed and closed the cases. Then she went to the door, her hands trembling, and turned the key.

He was waiting for her, of course. She had known that there was no way he was going to let her leave without facing him. He took one look at her clothes and the cases and anger flamed in his eyes.

'And just where the hell do you think you're going?'

'Home. Back to England,' Cordelia replied steadily.

'You're not going anywhere. You and I have some talking to do,' he told her grimly.

'No, there's nothing to say. May I use your phone to call for a taxi, please?'

'No, you damn well may not!'

'All right, then I'll walk.'

She bent to pick up her cases, but Marcus swore and wrenched them out of her hands, then he grabbed her wrist and pulled her after him as he strode through the house and out into the garden, almost making her fall down the steps as he dragged her along.

'Stop! Let me go!' Cordelia tried to pull away, but he hauled her along until they were well away from the house. Then he swung her round to face him.

'Now perhaps you'll tell me why you ran away without even bothering to leave a note?' he demanded with scarcely controlled violence.

'You know darn well why.' Cordelia tried to get her wrist free but he kept a tight grip on it. 'Because you're married!'

'You mean because Sugin told you I was married.'

Cordelia stopped struggling and stared at him. 'What do you mean? She showed me a photograph of you and your wife.'

Marcus's mouth drew into a thin line. 'Of my ex-wife. We were divorced over a year ago.'

'Divorced?'

'Yes.'

Cordelia gazed at him, her head whirling. She moved her hand and this time he released it. Then she turned on her heel and began to hurry back towards the house.

'Where are you going?'

'I told you, back to England.'

In two strides he caught her up and placed himself in front of her. 'But why? After what I've told you?'

'Because it doesn't make any difference. You weren't honest with me.' Her voice broke. 'I thought that everything between us was open and wonderful. That we had no secrets from one another. You—you taught me not to be shy or inhibited, and I held nothing back from you. While all the time you were . . .'

'Listen, Cordelia.' Marcus took hold of her shoulders and spoke urgently. 'What we had was so perfect that I didn't want to spoil it. I wanted it to go on that way for as long as possible. Okay, maybe it was selfish of me, but I'd been through such hell, and we were so perfect together that . . .'

'Stop it!' Tears running down her face, Cordelia tried to hit out at him. 'I don't want to hear any more. I don't believe a word of it. I bet all the time we were making love you were comparing me to her.' She sobbed and struggled futilely against his imprisoning hands. 'Is she better in bed than I am—is she?'

'Oh, my love. My sweet, darling idiot!' Marcus tried to take her in his arms, but she wouldn't let him.

'Don't call me that. You don't love me. You've never said you love me.'

'That isn't true. I've told you many times.'

Cordelia stopped struggling and glared at him. 'Only—only when we were having sex. And that doesn't count.'

An amused look came into his grey-blue eyes. 'Is that what you think? You couldn't be more wrong.' Putting a hand on either side of her tear-stained face, he said steadily and firmly, 'I love you, Cordelia, with all my heart. I want to marry you and have from the first night we spent together. I admit that at first I wasn't sure that I wanted to marry again, because you were so young, and because having failed once there's always the fear that you might fail again. But I loved and wanted you so much that I had to take you, and then I found that we had something very special going for us, something I didn't want to spoil. Which is why I held back telling you.'

'Oh, Marcus!' He felt her body tremble, and then she walked into his arms. 'You big fool! If you don't kiss me this minute I'll just go crazy!'

So he did, with a passion that left her in no doubt of his feelings.

Some time later, when he had kissed away her tears and brought a flush to her cheeks again, Marcus sat on the grass with his back against the trunk of a tree and pulled her down on to his lap.

'Tell me about your wife,' Cordelia said softly. 'Just this once, and I'll never ask again.'

He shrugged. 'It's the usual story. We got married when we were far too young and grew apart. I'd just left university and was working in the kind of job that had good career prospects and a strong social life. But then I gave it up to write and she didn't like that, or the loss in money. There were rows. She wouldn't go out to work and made it difficult for me to work at home. We parted and then had a reconciliation after I had a couple of best-sellers. But she wouldn't come abroad with me when I wanted to do research and was always accepting invitations for me to give lectures or attend literary parties when all I wanted to do was write. So we split again and lived apart for two years so that we could qualify for a divorce—which is one of the reasons I came here.' A dark, brooding look came into his eyes and his arms tightened around her. 'The break-up of a marriage is a kind of hell of its own. You come out of it feeling old and battered and that nothing will ever be really good again. But then,' he added softly, his hand in her curls, 'a girl comes along with the sun in her smile and in her hair, and suddenly you come alive again.'

Cordelia put up a finger to smooth the lines

around his mouth and saw the shadows of remembered pain in his eyes. 'I'm sorry I ran away,' she said softly. 'But when you're very much in love you don't always think rationally and you're—you're very vulnerable.'

'Do you think I don't know?'

'Oh, Marcus!' Her arms went round his neck and they kissed lingeringly. Something brushed against her arm and Cordelia glanced up, then she gave a laugh of pure happiness. 'Hey, do you see which tree we're sitting under?'

Following her gaze, Marcus looked upwards and saw the white blossoms of the frangipani glowing like milk-white pearls in the sun. He grinned. 'And do you realise just how long it's been since . . .'

'Oh, yes,' Cordelia assured him feelingly. 'I most certainly do!'

'So what, woman, do you intend to do about it?'

She smiled at him, her eyes alight with love and happiness. 'What do you suggest?' He pulled her closer and whispered in her ear. Cordelia's eyebrows rose. 'Here? Now?'

'What's wrong with here and now?'

'Nothing. Nothing in the world.' And she gave herself happily to his embrace.

YOURS absolutely FREE
Mills & Boon Catalogue

We know you enjoyed this Mills & Boon Romance. So we'd like to tell you all about the whole range of other exciting titles we offer – titles we know you wouldn't want to miss!

The Mills & Boon Catalogue offers you a fantastic selection of Romantic fiction written by the world's leading authors. Longer Romances offering you nearly four hundred pages of passion and intrigue. Dr/Nurse Romances for a truly romantic look at the world of medicine and our Masquerade Series to whisk you away to bygone ages. There is also a selection from our Romance Series, PLUS a whole range of exciting bargain book offers!

What are you waiting for? For your FREE Mills & Boon Catalogue simply complete and send the coupon to:– MILLS & BOON READER SERVICE, P.O. BOX 236, THORNTON ROAD, CROYDON, SURREY, CR9 3RU, ENGLAND. OR why not telephone us on 01-684 2141 and we will send you your catalogue by return of post.

Please note:– READERS IN SOUTH AFRICA write to Mills & Boon Ltd., Postbag X3010, Randburg 2125, S. Africa.

— — — — — — — — — — — — — — — —

Please send me my FREE Mills & Boon Catalogue.

NAME (Mrs/Miss) _____ EP5

ADDRESS _____

COUNTY/COUNTRY _____

POSTCODE _____

BLOCK LETTERS PLEASE